CW01095637

COMPOSTING
MASTERCLASS

Copyright © 2022 Tony O'Neill (Simplify Gardening)

All rights reserved. No part of this book may be reproduced
or used in any manner without the prior written permission of
the copyright owner except for the use of brief quotations in
a book review.

To request permissions, contact the publisher at
publisher@simplifygardening.com
or complete the contact form at simplifygardening.com

Hardcover ISBN 978-1-7397793-0-6
Paperback ISBN 978-1-7397793-1-3
Audiobook ISBN 978-1-7397793-2-0
eBook ISBN 978-1-7397793-3-7

First Paperback Edition April 2022
Edited by Courtney Goldsmith
Cover art and layout by SpiffingCovers.com
Images by Tony O'Neill, Rhys Jones, Edwin Corbett

Publisher Simplify Gardening LTD
publisher@simplifygardening.com
simplifygardening.com

COMPOSTING MASTERCLASS

Feed the soil not your plants!

TONY O'NEILL

TESTIMONIALS

Tony O'Neill has created a definitive work that will find a welcome home in any gardener's library. Tony expertly confronts common misperceptions and misunderstandings and shines a light on research-based composting methods for gardeners of all skill levels. Compost bins and compost piles are ubiquitous in gardens around the world and for many gardeners composting is often a mysterious chore. Along with his personal experiences offered in conversational prose, the science behind effective composting is easy to read and understandable for every reader.

Many experienced gardening educators know that healthy soil is a key to gardening success and Tony devotes the necessary attention to not just compost but it's critical role in improving garden soil and the science behind its effectiveness. As I encountered Tony's descriptions and explanations throughout the book, I wondered if he would discuss each of the composting methods that I have discovered in more than 30 years of gardening. He didn't disappoint and not only did I find these time-proven processes with each turn of the page, but I found the mathematics and physics behind them to be exciting and enticing. This incredible book will be a cherished reference source for me as I prepare future lessons and presentations on the subject. For new gardeners looking to learn the basics of compost or for experienced ones like me, there is a bountiful harvest of information in this book.

Scott Wilson (Gardener Scott)

The most comprehensive book on composting I have ever read!

I thought I knew a thing or two about composting organic materials to use back in my garden as "black gold" but Tony's breaking down (pun intended) of composting principals and methods has given me a better understanding of the whole process.

If you want to know everything there is about composting and becoming a Compost Master – read this book!

Mark Valencia (Self Sufficient Me)

I found Tony's book to be chock full of great analogies, that for me, bring life to concepts through a visual image in my mind! It helped me absorb the vast amounts of incredible data contained in it.

As an adjunct to Tony's book, the course will help solidify my understanding of the content!! There is a load of information, all valuable, and it will take repetitive access for me to grasp these methodologies, truly!

Tony's advice is for seriously dedicated composters wanting to become a master of their craft, and I've no doubt that's what people can be, if they apply the principles contained therein!

The methods he discusses are not just beneficial to one's growing space but explore practices that, if adopted by the individual and agricultural community, can change the very conditions of our planet at large!

This book is not only easy to read, but it's in language that even I felt comfortable as a novice!

Tony's book showed me how I could better impact my soil quality and have a more productive garden while saving money. I cannot think of any gardener, big or small, that could not benefit from reading this fantastic book.

It is indeed a master class on composting and a reference tool that turns a fine craft into a work of art!

Chris Savage (Exploring Nature Together)

Composting Masterclass is a comprehensive guide to making compost. From the basics to the science, Tony walks you through the why and the how (and how not) of creating your own compost packed full of microbes and soil-life enhancing materials.

Liz Zorab (Byther Farm)

"Tony not only has an incredible knowledge about gardening, but he shares this knowledge in a way that anyone can understand. The information he provides on YouTube will make you a better gardener, regardless of whether you have been gardening all your life or just planted your first seed.

Composting is such a fundamental aspect of garden but is often overlooked. I have read many books on composting and thought there couldn't be much more to learn. I was wrong. Tony's book demonstrates a depth and breadth of knowledge that kept me interested until the very last word. This book is certainly a Master Class in Composting."

Shaun Hurst (Chillichump)

DEDICATION

This book is dedicated to my friend Brian Bastable who sadly lost his battle to cancer in November 2021. Brian was such an amazing person, he was one of my first supporters and became my very first admin of the Facebook group, later joining the presenting team on my YouTube channel (Simplify Gardening). It is amazing to think that we had just 5,000 subscribers when Brian left to start a new career with the customs office. He was always talking about his daughter Emily, son Patrick and his mum Yvonne. His family was his world.

I remember we both went to the Spring Malvern Gardening Show as presenters and the whole day we shared stories about his mum and Emily. He was so proud he was a dad, and he was an amazing dad. He adored Emily and everything he did was for her. Emily, if you ever read this, know your dad loved you more that you will ever know!

RIP Brian, you were a great friend and helped Simplify Gardening become what it is today. I will never forget our friendship.

ACKNOWLEDGMENTS

I have wanted to write this book for a very long time, but I have always put it off due to other commitments. I am so glad I took the time to finally put pen to paper and hopefully provide a resource that will help all gardeners to understand the process of composting. None of this would be possible without the continued support of my family, and friends. Firstly, I would like to thank my beautiful wife Tina who has been my rock for the past 14 years no matter what crazy ideas I have had. You have been there for me every step of the way, encouraging and lifting me up when times have been hard. Thank you, baby, for all your support I love you. Next to my three beautiful children. Wayne, Caitlyn, and Amber who have all missed time with me for me to realise the dream of writing this book. I love all three of you more than you will ever know.

I would like to thank some friends who have also been there helping along the way. Writing a book can be a challenge and putting your ideas into print is a culmination of many people's supports. Chris Savage, Liz Zorab, Shaun Hurst and Scott Wilson, each of you have sat for hours by phone, email and live chats listening to me and my ideas, you will never know the strength you provided especially when I struggled learning the steps required to become an author. Thank you!

To one of my best friends from my childhood, Dr Rhys Jones, thank you providing some of the images included within this book. I know we don't see much of each other due to the timescales of life, but I know you will be there if I ever need it. Thank you pal.

A massive thank you to my team who have supported me for years, whether that was admin for Facebook groups or the writers that help me on my website, simplifygardening.com. You have all been amazing especially Edwin Corbett who has been like a right arm to me. You are all amazing!

Last and not least a massive thank you to my parents and brother. Elaine Edward and Edward Jr. You have not only brought me up to be a decent human being who tries to help others, but you have been there throughout all the challenges life has brought me. I love you both very much and although I never say it, I need you to know you both mean the world to me. Same goes for you bro. Thank you for always being there no matter what.

CONTENTS

INTRODUCTION

There are few things as satisfying as watching a person practicing a craft they have mastered and love. They seem to have the innate ability to *sense* a process, straddling the spheres of science, art, and intuition simultaneously. It is only through years of formal practice that the musical maestro gains the privilege of improv – and it all starts with a thorough knowledge of the fundamentals. For master gardeners, the same holds true.

Unfortunately, in becoming a master, you may face some challenges finding reliable access to the fundamentals of learning. While the internet has exponentially expanded our access to knowledge, you'll rarely find everything you need in a single source. Also, the internet is rife with misinformation. Many contributors merely reprocess the opinions of their peers. Upon each repetition, *facts* can morph into click-bait fiction.

My name is Tony O'Neill, and I'm passionate about gardening. For as long as I can remember, gardening has been a constant feature in my life, providing endless satisfaction and a sense of wellbeing. If you're familiar with my **Simplify Gardening** website and YouTube channel, you'll know that I love sharing my discoveries. In writing this book, I wanted to bring gardeners a consolidated, simplified learning source for an essential gardener's skill – soil health development.

If you are among the fortunate few, you have some power to define your environment. However, most people's lives are a constant exercise at extracting meaning while navigating the risks that their environments bring. As ingenious as plants are, *their* environment is subject to the gardener's skill set. A master gardener can reduce environmental risks while maximizing growth opportunities for flora and fauna in their garden.

While most gardeners are familiar with the plant aspects of gardening, only a few fully appreciate the essential work of microorganisms and other creatures living in their garden's soil. The marvelous thing about nature is its propensity to reproduce, even against the odds. If, however, we take better care of our plants' environment, especially what happens at the root level, nature's response will be even more bountiful.

But mastership is only partially in the head and heart; it also manifests in the hands (or in the voice, for singers and orators). While I could lose myself in awe at the paradoxical delicateness and robustness of nature, helping gardeners become masters at their craft will require practical guidance. This book offers all the essential technical knowledge (head), passionate petitioning (heart), and great practical advice on how-to (hand).

It's impossible to overemphasize the importance of composting, both for your garden and the general environment. As such, your skill at creating good compost, using various methods, materials, and microorganisms, is inextricably linked to becoming a master gardener. Together, we will explore all the domains of this vast topic in detail.

I have made every effort to ensure both novice and experienced gardeners will benefit from this book. I have tried to tier practical learning and theoretical information progressively throughout. The final chapter is purely academic. I have purposefully placed it at the back of the book to avoid cluttering applied learning with non-essential but interesting information.

This book consists of two parts. In the first section, we delve into what compost is and explore what all the fuss is about. I've interlaced this first section with anecdotal references to my own learning curve. In doing so, I hope to interrupt the monotony of technical discourse and provide reference points to your journey of discovery. In working through this section, it's worth remembering that nature has daily, seasonal, and annual cycles and notoriously plays the long game. In an era of instant gratification, high demands on our limited attention bandwidth, and over-scheduled lives, the adjustment to nature's schedule is a conscious one.

Please bear with me in my constant analogies between composting, orchestras, and symphonies, but the similarities are striking. The soil food web has hierarchies of consumers; an orchestra has tiers of instruments and tones. There is complete synergy between the different players, where the whole is bigger than the sum of its individual unique parts. And most importantly, not all players play at the same time. Bacteria have been around for three and a half billion years – people for an estimated six million years (0.17%). Bacteria are all around and only become active when the environment suits them. As the conductor's baton directs musicians in an orchestra, the gardener's skills can activate different microorganisms at different times for their own purposes. The second section explores how to activate and reproduce microorganisms effectively.

In the second section, we explore the how-to of composting. We look at the different forms of compost, the tools needed to create healthy compost, and the pros and cons of each method. By combining various materials, managing the timing of different sub-processes, and using alternative techniques, we can produce composts for specific uses. I'll provide you with the plans for composting facilities that suit your unique requirements. You can select what will work for you based on your available time, materials, space, and the level of effort you wish to invest (or not).

There is a selection of composting methods, each producing a unique set of microorganisms with specific benefits. Add to those variables the materials you could use for composting, each with its particular carbon, nitrogen, and moisture content, and bioavailability. With all these variables multiplied, the possible alternative approaches become almost infinite. Managing the impact of these variable combinations requires solid guidelines – we will establish what these are for most circumstances.

While this book is sufficiently comprehensive to be used as a single source of learning, using it in combination with my Composting Masterclass Course will benefit visual learners. I sincerely hope that this book (and the course) will be a definitive milestone for becoming a highly skilled gardener – a master of your craft.

1. WHAT IS COMPOSTING

COMPOSTING IN NATURE

Composting is the natural reduction and transformation of dead plant- and animal matter to humus. Humus (a Latin word for earth) is the dark-brown organic matter formed from decaying plant or animal material. Consider what would happen if fallen trees over the centuries didn't rot. Imagine the health risks if animals that died of diseases didn't decompose.

Decomposition is nature's way of recovering the essential organic building blocks from the dead for the benefit of the living – a process of perpetual renewal.

Nature is a closed-loop system where the health of the soil, plants, animals, people, environment, and the planet is inseparable. It's one continuum of interrelated events. In the absence of human interference, nature follows repeating production, reduction, reintegration, and regeneration cycles. While these cycles are easily observed in seasonal changes, these are macro- and micro-interactions that are less obvious yet play a crucial role.

Recent studies show that forests inhabited by larger mammals are less prone to devastating forest fires. The manure produced by these animals promotes improved surface growth and moisture levels. At a micro-level, the added compost increases the microorganism populations, which improves soil structure and health—improved soil health results in improved ground cover and moisture retention. The symbiotic effect is a decrease in destructive fire hazards.

Each tier in the food chain has distinct, often incidental, functions. The rodents (squirrels) and primates (monkeys) in trees help shake the trees, causing leaves to fall. These leaves are rich in carbohydrates and protein and help provide essential pre-winter food for the larger mammals. The larger mammals (deer) eat the leaves and deposit manure and nitrogen-rich urine. Their hooves also shred the leaves, aiding decomposition rates.

Fungi more easily decompose the shredded leaves, and the abundance of fungi aids in breaking down larger wood pieces such as dead branches and fallen trees. As the leaves and wood decompose, the resulting humus provides:

- *Habitat for other microorganism populations.*
- *Improving the forest floor's pH.*
- *Water holding capacity.*
- *Erosion resistance.*

The improved soil health improves the plants' health, strengthening their food production capacities. Healthier foliage and grass can support larger herds – a cycle towards optimal livelihoods in balance.

The decomposition and final stabilization of organic matter by biological action constantly occur in nature. The accumulation of fallen trees, dead animals, animal feces and urine, and plant debris naturally pile up, decompose and increase soil fertility. Gardeners utilize the process to dispose of and reclaim organic waste material hygienically. We call this process composting and the final product compost.

ORCHESTRATED COMPOSTING

Composting is also a hygienic process of developing a soil food web (soil biota) by causing the proliferation of microorganisms (bacteria and fungi) in a controlled environment using organic waste materials. The stable organic matter improves the soil structure and water management abilities and hosts the soil biota. But the increased fertility, disease resilience, and erosion control can all be directly ascribed to microorganisms. In this sense, composting is more about farming microorganisms than stabilizing organic matter.

As gardeners, we can improve the health of our soil naturally (as opposed to synthetically). However, not everyone knows that soil fertility is a direct product of soil-dwelling organisms, collectively referred to as the soil biota. We need to understand that compost is more than a soil augmentation. Composting is the development of healthy soil biota – an essential ecosystem for soil productivity and health.

There are millions of bacteria and fungi types. Most of them are present in every composting mix – *present but not necessarily active*. As the environment changes, microorganisms suitable for those specific conditions become active and reproduce. Bacteria are prolific reproducers, and a single cell may "parent" billions of individual cells in a couple of hours.

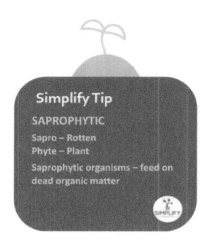

Simplify Tip

SAPROPHYTIC

Sapro – Rotten
Phyte – Plant

Saprophytic organisms – feed on dead organic matter

Generally speaking, there are two composting processes: (a) Aerobic decomposition and stabilization and (b) Anaerobic fermentation (carbohydrates) or putrefaction (proteins). In both methods, different saprophytic organisms feed on dying, dead, or decaying organic materials, converting them into a more stable form of organic matter. While composting is either aerobic or anaerobic, some bacteria can grow in aerobic and anaerobic conditions but grow better under one condition.

In this book, we will review variations of both aerobic and anaerobic processes. For instance, where does Bokashi fit in? Or vermicomposting? We will also examine how different materials affect different techniques. As an example, what is the difference between using grass clippings in trench composting, static piles, or hot composting? Read on to discover the answers.

2. WHY COMPOSTING?

In this chapter, we'll review the four most crucial spheres of composting: (a) Its impact on soils, (b) its impact on vegetations, (c) its benefits as a waste management process, and finally (d) the essential role of composting in eco-sustainability.

Knowing how to develop healthy soil should be a life skill taught at schools. Composting is the best available means of improving soil health. Creating healthy soil does not require land – it can be done in apartments too. You can fill your indoor space with pot plants and vertical gardens by using kitchen scraps, cultivated microorganisms, and store-bought ground. Increasing indoor vegetation is known to contribute to improved mental and physical health. Creating healthy soil not only benefits plants but it benefits the environment holistically. Composting is a meaningful, easy, and effective way of reversing some of the negative impacts humans have on our environment and planet. It is also the best option for improving soil health – feeding not only the plant, but also the soil.

25 REASONS WHY COMPOSTING IS ESSENTIAL FOR A HEALTHY GARDEN

1. IT IS A PREFERRED WAY TO RECYCLE DEAD PLANT MATERIAL

Death holds the franchise for life – at some point, everything dies. Decomposition is the default process for any organism that has recently died. Alternatives include consumption by fire or preservation by freezing. Managed composting is the most effective way to benefit from the natural process of decomposition.

2. AEROBIC COMPOSTING REDUCES PATHOGENS AND UNWANTED SEEDS RAPIDLY

The temperatures at which thermophilic bacteria and fungi thrive are above the thermal survival threshold of seeds and common troublesome pathogens. Composting is a highly effective way to cull pathogen populations in soil.

3. TO INCREASE THE AVAILABILITY OF NUTRIENTS TO PLANTS

The soil food web development promoted by composting provides a tiered hierarchy of consumers. In the consumption of materials and organisms of a lower order, nitrogen is absorbed and stored. At the same time, carbon is consumed and burnt off, releasing CO_2. The result is the sequential reduction of essential minerals to a form that plants can use.

4. TO SUPPORT, OPTIMIZE, AND BALANCE SOIL FAUNA AND MICROORGANISM POPULATIONS

The development, growth, culling, and regrowth of fauna and microorganisms is reasonably predictable in composting processes. The sequential staged growth and latency of different organisms have a biological reset effect.

5. TO REPAIR AND IMPROVE SOIL COMPOSITION AND STRUCTURE

The 12 soil types are defined by the sample's represented clay, silt, and sand percentage. For clay, compost will reduce anaerobic conditions by decreasing specific gravity and increasing porosity. For sand, compost will improve texture and strengthen binding bonds. For silt, compost will reduce its tendency towards being a dilatant fluid, aerating the mass.

6. LIMIT EROSION, RUNOFF, LEACHING, AND COMPACTION

Organisms in compost produce compounds that bind grains of soil, preventing **erosion**. The need for less additional synthetic fertilizer reduces the risk of runoff that contaminates water sources. Improved hydrophilic action is a function of mold and reduces the draining of nutrients through leaching.

Studies have shown that building sites, notorious for compaction by mechanical action, can fully recover by merely adding a top composting layer. Compost aids in the formation of aggregates, which are clusters of soil particles that aid in the structure of the soil. Air, moisture, and nutrients are all held together in the soil's many tiny air channels and pores.

7. TO REHABILITATE DAMAGED SOIL

Soil microbes have demonstrated their ability to replenish leached or lost nutrients over time. In most cases, this process occurs over two to three years. Improved conditions for soil microbes, such as more food, air, and water, as well as less habitat disruption, can help the soil function better. Considering the full requirements of the soil system is essential in remediating ill-functioning soil and improving soil quality and productivity. This includes the soil structure, chemistry, and the soil biome.

8. IMPROVE SOIL TILTH AND PRODUCTIVE CAPACITY

A key feature of compost with balanced microorganisms is that it further enhances good agricultural practices like green composting. Rhizobia, for instance, has a symbiotic relationship with legumes, exchanging fixed nitrogen for amino acids.

9. TO FACILITATE OPTIMIZED SOIL PH VARIABILITY

Aerobic composting has a pH buffering function that can adapt soil acidity to environmental requirements. The microorganisms cause the pH to fluctuate within a range of 5.5 and 7.2.

10. MAINTAIN OPTIMAL RATIOS OF FUNGI, BACTERIA, AND NEMATODES IN SOIL

Ecosystems have the ability, if not interfered with, to self-regulate towards stability. For instance, some fungi destroy pathogenic fungi; actinomycetes produce antibiotics that limit the development of bacteria; and nematodes can act as transporters of bacteria, ensuring their better distribution.

11. MAINTAIN OPTIMAL RATIOS OF PREDATOR/PREY IN THE SOIL BIOTA

The introduction of stable, diversified microorganisms into your garden improves the health of the soil biota ecosystem, ensuring a balance between predator and prey populations.

12. OPTIMIZE NUTRIENT CYCLING AND MICRONUTRIENT UPTAKE

During composting, organic materials do not merely undergo processes of degradation. Microorganisms reduce complex compounds into monomers (monosaccharides, amino acids, etc.), reconstituting these into bioavailable compounds. The activity also involves re-synthesis and polymerization reactions to create a product that is intricately beneficial to soil health and plant life.

13. MAXIMIZE NUTRIENT DENSITY

The composting process reduces and redefines organic matter. Even though a compost pile may start with a carbon to nitrogen ratio (C:N) of 30:1, the end product could be as low as 10:1. This implies a greater concentration of nutritious nitrogen per volume.

14. SEQUESTER EXCESS ATMOSPHERIC CARBON

A study by UC Davis has shown that soil carbon content increased by as much as 26% over two decades. This was true even to depths of 6 feet. Carbon has to filter through soil microbes to create stabilized forms of carbon in soil. Composting is the best available option for sequestering atmospheric carbon.[1]

---

1   https://caes.ucdavis.edu/news/compost-key-sequestering-carbon-soil

15. INCREASE CROP IMMUNITY

Beneficial microbes in compost can suppress soil and foliar pathogens. Making compost tea and using this in a diluted form acts as a barrier to leaf infections.

16. SUPPORT PLANT-POLLINATOR POPULATIONS

Many roadside turf programs have adopted composting as a critical feature to increase pollinator populations. The reduced need for pesticides further improves both roots and shoots, as well as the ecosystem around the plant.

17. MANAGE PEST POPULATIONS WITHOUT PESTICIDES

Compost radically reduces the need for chemical pesticides as the microorganisms protect plants from pests and diseases. The predator/prey sequence referred to in benefit number 11 extends to the roots and the plant's shoots.

18. MANAGE WEEDS WITHOUT HERBICIDES

Weeds are non-beneficial plants that only contribute 20% carbon to microorganisms. Compare this to grass (60%), vegetables (75%), and trees (82%). When microorganisms help plants thrive, competitors are less likely to succeed. Also, aerobic temperatures neutralize seeds, including weed seeds. Incorporating weeds in your compost can progressively reduce weeds by 90% per annum.

19. IMPROVE FLAVOR AND NUTRITION IN EDIBLE PLANTS, FRUITS, AND SEEDS FOR ANIMALS AND HUMANS

Synthetic fertilizers often lack the macro and micronutrients found in compost. The nutritional value of plants is increased by these soil-borne nutrients. Composting enriches the soil with nutrients, reducing the need for pesticides and fertilizers. Pesticides and fertilizers require fossil fuels for their production. Some are potentially harmful to your health.

Comparative studies of organic crops show they have a significantly higher presence of antioxidants. These include flavones (+26%), stilbenes (+28%), flavanols (+50%), phenolic acid (+19%), flavanones (+69%), and anthocyanins (+51%).

20. CONCENTRATE AND RETAIN GROWTH FORCES

Soil health is critical to the preservation (and remediation) of our waterways. Increased water retention and reduced runoff are two benefits of composting. Effective microorganisms successfully remediate polluted water sources.

21. INCREASE SOIL GAS AND WATER HOLDING CAPACITY

Microorganisms aid in the formation of aggregates (clusters of soil particles) that benefit soil structure and reduce erosion. Tiny channels and pores are formed in the process, increasing the soil's capacity to retain air, moisture, and nutrients.

22. REDUCE ODOR, FLY, AND OTHER VECTOR PROBLEMS

Uncontrolled decomposition conditions include the presence of egg-laying flies, anaerobic conditions, foul odors, and seepage. Controlled aerobic composting with sufficient oxygenation, controlled humidity, and effective pile structure and turning eliminates these conditions.

23. TO IMPROVE ENVIRONMENTAL HYGIENE

Rotting plants and food waste attract rodents and flies and can smell like rotting eggs (hydrogen sulfide), vinegar, or rancid butter (butyric acid). Composting food scraps, garden cuttings, and lawn clippings is an effective way to manage hygiene risks. Bokashi, a fermentation process, helps households manage kitchen waste effectively and hygienically.

24. LIMIT WASTAGE OF VALUABLE RESOURCES

Reusing freely available resources such as leaves, weeds, and grass trimmings to produce compost, a substance with known benefits, makes perfect sense. Sending these resources to landfills creates unmanaged anaerobic conditions that pour methane and hydrogen sulfides into the atmosphere. Not only does dumping these resources have no benefit, but it also actually causes environmental harm.

25. CONTRIBUTE TO HEALTHIER WATER RESERVES

Nitrogen and pesticide runoff from yards and farms causes untold damage to our water reserves. Compost enriches the soil and retains fertilizer more effectively, providing less fertilizer runoff. Compost also acts as a buffer, neutralizing both alkaline and acidic soils, bringing pH levels to an optimized range for plant nutrient availability.

BENEFICIAL IMPACT OF COMPOST ON SOIL

MINERAL PORTION OF SOIL

The inorganic part of soil consists of deconstructed rock, tiny mineral particles called clay, silt, and sand, each identified by their particle size. Imagine a grain of sand is the size of a baseball; then, comparatively, a particle of silt would be a size of a pea and a particle of clay the size of a pinhead. Depending on the representative ratio of each of these, soil texture could be defined as:

- Clay
- Silty Clay
- Silty Clay Loam
- Clay Loam
- Sandy Clay
- Sandy Clay Loam
- Sandy Loam
- Loam
- Silt Loam
- Silt
- Loamy Sand
- Sand

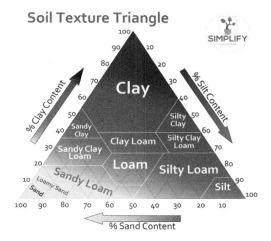

If you wish to test your soil texture, here are four guidelines:

- When wet, a sandy soil's texture is gritty, and a ball made of it will crumble easily.

- Soil that is both gritty and easy to work is called loamy; it is composed of sand, silt, and clay, and when it is moist, it forms a ball that holds its shape but breaks apart when squeezed.

- It's easy to break apart silty soil, and when it dries, it looks like flour. When wet, silty soils are slippery and do not form a ribbon when pinched between the fingers and thumb.

- In clay soil, large, hard clods are formed, and cracks appear on the surface. When wet, clay soils feel squishy and pliable. A ribbon can be created when the soil is moist by pinching it between the thumb and fingers. A more significant amount of clay is indicated by a longer ribbon that forms before it breaks.

Below are the characteristics of the different base textures:

Characteristic	Clay	Silt	Sand
Looseness	Poor	Fair	Good
Water and Air Space	Poor	Fair	Good
Water Management	Poor Drainage	Fair	Poor water retention
Clod Forming Inclination	Good	Fair	Poor
Workability	Poor	Fair	Poor
Fertility	Fair to Good	Fair	Poor
Cation-Exchange Capacity (CEC)	Good	Poor	Poor

Clay	When Dry:	Clods cannot be broken with fingers without some pressure.
	When Moist:	Relatively malleable and sticky when wet; leaves residue on fingers.
	Composition:	Sand: 0 - 45%, Silt: 0 - 40%, Clay: 40 - 100%
Sandy Clay Loam	When Dry:	Clods are difficult to break with fingers.
	When Moist:	Feels slightly gritty; leaves residue on fingers; ribbons reasonably well.
	Composition:	Sand: 45 - 80%, Silt: 0 - 28%, Clay: 20 - 35%
Silty Clay Loam	When Dry:	Same as Sandy Clay Loam.
	When Moist:	Is very smooth; stains fingers; ribbons fairly well.
	Composition:	Sand: 0 - 20%, Silt: 40 - 73%, Clay: 27 - 40%
Clay Loam	When Dry:	Very difficult to break clods with fingers.
	When Moist:	Feels slightly gritty; leaves residue on fingers; ribbons relatively well.
	Composition:	Sand: 20 - 45%, Silt: 15 - 53%, Clay: 27 - 40%
Silt Loam	When Dry:	Difficult to break clods; if pulverized, the powder feels soft and smooth. Leaves residue on fingers.
	When Moist:	Has a slick, buttery feel; stains fingers.
	Composition:	Sand: 0 - 50%, Silt: 50 - 88%, Clay: 0 - 27%

	When Dry:	Moderately difficult to break clods; relatively gritty.
Loam	When Moist:	Can form a ball that breaks easily.
	Composition:	Sand: 23 - 52%, Silt: 28 - 50%, Clay: 7 - 27%
	When Dry:	Clods brake easily; sand is visible.
Sandy Loam	When Moist:	Gritty; forms a ball that can be handled with care; residue definitely left on fingers.
	Composition:	Sand: 43 - 85%, Silt: 0 - 50%, Clay: 0 - 20%
	When Dry:	Clay and silt may obscure sand; it feels loose but gritty.
Loamy Sand	When Moist:	Feels gritty; forms easily crumbled ball; light residue of fingers when handled.
	Composition:	Sand: 70 - 90%, Silt: 0 - 30%, Clay: 0 - 15%
	When Dry:	Loose and flows from hand.
Sand	When Moist:	Balls formed will crumble at the slightest touch.
	Composition:	Sand: 85 - 100%, Silt: 0 - 15%, Clay: 0 - 10%

SOIL COMPOSITION AND THE ROLE OF COMPOST

When it comes to sustaining life on planet earth, soil is the foundation for everything. This comparatively thin outer layer also serves as a habitat for crucial microorganisms. The primary decomposers in terrestrial ecosystems, soil microbial communities, play a vital role in soil nutrient cycling and energy flows. They can be sensitive to and influential in predicting small changes in soil ecosystems. They are the foundation of soil ecological function.

A generalized organic and inorganic mix ratio is 45% minerals, 25% air, 25% water, and 5% organic matter within the top 18 inches. Our consideration of the above ratios is because compost has an almost magical balancing effect for all of the above.

Compost aerates clay for improved soil textures, accommodating air and aerobic microorganisms; it improves sand's water-holding ability and increases its organic matter; and it manages water and air content for optimal organic activity in silt. Without a doubt, compost is a wonder product that brings soil biology to environments that would otherwise be mostly sterile. Compost's further benefits for mineral soil are the reduction of erosion susceptibility, increased cation-exchange capacity, pH buffering capabilities, and improved soil tilth.

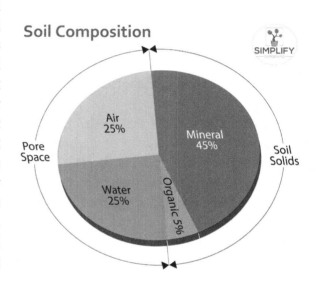

REDUCED EROSION SUSCEPTIBILITY

Soil is a three-part open system with solids, liquids, and gasses, with strong interaction between each of the parts. Primary soil particles, particularly silt and sand, would be prone to erosion if they were not cemented together in groupings called peds or aggregates. The shape and strength of the aggregates influence pore size, distribution, and water and gas holding capacities. However, the binding matter used by bacteria, fungi, and actinomycetes has built-in channels, ensuring continued porosity for air movement and moisture management.

CATION-EXCHANGE CAPACITY (CEC)

Cation-exchange capacity (CEC) is a fundamental soil property, influencing nutrient availability, soil structure stability, reaction to fertilizers and other ameliorants, and soil pH. It's an indicator of the soil's ability to hold positively charged ions.

Opposites attract; at least in electronics this is true. Like magnets, negatively charged soil particles attract positively charged molecules. These molecules could be water, soil amendments, or nutrients. Attraction due to either positive or negative charges is called the cation-exchange capacity (CEC). If the soil's CEC value is low, few molecules are attracted to the soil particle's surface. Obviously, the opposite is true too – good attraction, good chemistry.

For now, with some writer's creative liberty, we can generalize and throw out the following basic guidelines. When you have your soil analyzed (tested), the report will have your CEC value listed. Sand has the lowest (about 10) CEC, and clay has the highest (25). However, if you add organic matter, the very best CEC (100) becomes a possibility. The electrical activity in leaf mold, for instance, is so high it can power a small gadget.

The CEC keeps water from draining from clay, and its absence allows water to run through the sand at a rate of 20 inches per hour. Plants need access to water and nutrition. The correlation is direct – soil low in organic matter will have low cation-exchange capacities. A low molecule attraction capacity will lead to plants wilting sooner and underperforming generally. Again, compost is the solution.

BUFFER SALT EFFECT – PH BUFFERING

It doesn't matter if your soil is acidic or alkaline; compost can effectively correct the pH. The microorganisms' ability to influence pH is responsible for this buffering effect. Acidity levels are reliable indicators of soil health. Acidity directly impacts the yields of crops, their suitability, the availability of plant nutrients, and the activity of microorganisms in the soil.

Climate, mineral content, and soil texture are factors that cannot be altered. The soil's natural pH results from the interactions between various soil-forming factors (parent material, time, relief or topography, climate, and organisms). Minerals in the soil's parent material determine the pH of newly formed soils. Soil mineral weathering is controlled by temperature and rainfall. A process known as soil acidification occurs in warm, wet environments due to the leaching of rainwater into the soil. Due to less intense soil weathering and leaching in dry climates, pH can be neutral to alkaline.

Clay and organic matter-rich soils are better able to withstand changes in pH (buffering capacity) than sandy soils. Although clay content cannot be altered, organic matter content can be changed through management. Low organic matter content in sandy soils results in high water throughput, making them more susceptible to acidification than other soils. The addition of compost to any soil will positively affect the soil's health, including the pH.

COMPOST AND IMPROVED SOIL TILTH

Tilth is a term used to describe how the soil structure affects plant growth. Soil with healthy tilth has excellent drainage and water-holding capacity, making it ideal for plant growth and easy for gardeners to work. Bulk density, the weight per volume of soil, is also related to a tilth. Low-density soils have greater porosity and tilth than higher-density ones. Roots will penetrate and grow through well-aerated soils with ample pore space and even distribution of large and small pores. The larger pores are protected from clogging by loose particles thanks to the high aggregate stability.

Soil tilth is a central soil-health indicator and is often also referred to as friability or mellowness. When walked on, mellow soil will crumble and give a little. Soil with a healthy tilth is very easy to work with. On the other hand, ground with poor tilth can feel heavy, compacted, or overly sandy. As an indicator of soil health, tilth is critical.

Gardeners often talk about tilth, friability, and mellowness being hard to define with precision since they are so location specific. However, gardeners (and farmers) agree that working with soil with healthy tilth is a delight that is hard to describe until you work with soil without these characteristics.

HEALTHY TILTH HAS THE FOLLOWING CHARACTERISTICS:
- The soil has suitable aggregates, soil particles (i.e., sand, silt, and clay) held together in a single mass or cluster. Stable soil aggregates are a product of the binding action of compost (humus, soil organic matter, the activity of microorganisms) and the growth of plant roots in the soil. Natural aggregates are called peds. Clods are a product of tillage when underground soil biota activity is disturbed.

- Aggregate stability is the ability of natural aggregates to resist breaking apart. Aggregate destruction is mainly caused by tillage but can also be caused by water action. Soil is said to have poor aggregate stability if individual aggregates readily break apart.

- Soil consistency refers to the ease with which a lump can be crushed by the fingers.

Soil tilth and structure are directly impacted by how you manage your soil. Regular assessment of your soil's health will help you identify whether your current management practices promote or impede the free movement of water and air through the ground. The size of your earthworm population is a good indicator of healthy soil biota. It is important to note that rainfall is the most significant soil compacter. Adding compost to your soil and using it as a mulch is the quickest route to a healthy tilth. Avoid working with soil that is too wet, as this destroys aggregates.

COMPOST AND IMPROVED SOIL HEALTH
Listed below are the 10 most essential indicators of healthy soil. You will notice that compost plays the lead role in all 10 vital soil-health-building elements. State extension programs, supported by the USDA, have standardized soil quality assessments, mainly in support of farmers.

Surface Cover
Surface cover plays a vital role in minimizing weeds, preventing soil compaction due to rain, and further strengthening the soil microorganism population. Following a *See-no-Soil* policy is the most productive way towards healthier soil. Surface cover can either be a mulch or green compost (legumes as a growing ground cover). The role of compost is evident.

Soil Structure
The term soil structure refers to the combined elements of aggregates, tilth, and surface penetrability. An absence of clods (aggregate must easily crumb) and its ability to remain intact in water are indicators of healthy soil. Also, consider crusting on the soil surface that may prevent quick water absorption. In improving aggregate quality, soil tilth, and surface compaction, compost is the answer.

Organic Matter

Humus is the color of dark chocolate – not black nor caramel. Soil with a healthy portion of organic matter (at least 5% of the total dry matter weight) is dark brown. Adjusting your soil to reflect an abundant presence of organic matter may take a couple of seasons, but being forewarned allows you to work towards that goal.

Both agriculturists and archeologists use the Munsell soil color charts as a comparative color guide. Depending on the color of the soil in each area, the land's suitability for various purposes, the best crops to plant, the viability of wastewater systems, and other uses can be determined. The charts are adjusted to both dry and wet soil colors.

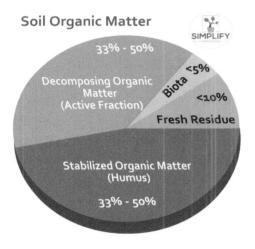

The percentage of decomposed plant and animal matter is called organic matter. It is expressed as a percentage of the soil material that is less than 0.08 inches (2mm) wide. As organic matter, such as manure, straw, or plant residue from a previous harvest decompose, it is added to the soil. When decay is active, organic matter will be in various stages of decomposition, from identifiable plant parts to individual plant fibers to dark chocolate brown humus.

Plant residue is decomposed by soil organisms and recycled in a variety of ways that benefit the soil. Microbial activity accounts for most of the soil decomposition. Soil microorganisms like bacteria and fungi benefit from the breakdown of the organic residue by larger soil organisms. Plant residue decomposition is a good indicator of the health of the soil's microbial community. The absence of a visible residue indicates that low residues were produced and returned to the earth. But an excessive amount of residue means soil organisms are unable to break down the material. The more significant parts of the decomposition process are preferred because they contribute to the soil's tilth and structure. In contrast, soil microorganisms feed on smaller pieces.

Organic matter is essential to soil quality because it increases the soil cation-exchange capacity (the ability to attract and hold vital nutrients and moisture). Microorganisms' activities in organic matter provide the glue to bind soil particles into aggregates improving water infiltration, soil structure, and tilth. Organic matter is a food source for a diverse population of soil biota (the ecosystem of living organisms in soil). The soil biota promotes air and water movement within the ground, as well as nutrient recycling. Organic material (and the surrounding soil biota) is the primary nitrogen and sulfur source (and supplies a significant part of the phosphorous requirements) for crops.

Soil Erosion

The start of soil erosion is evidenced by the formation of minor rivulets, called rills. Rills form when surface runoff's shear stress exceeds the soil's shear strength, limiting the soil's ability to resist forces acting across the surface. Water breaks up soil particles and carries them down the slope, causing the erosion process to begin.

Surface cover, using mulch or cover crops, is an adequate preventer of erosion. Erosion can only take place if water can sufficiently accumulate on the surface to start flowing. The soil's water infiltration properties improve the rapid absorption of rain, again a product of compost addition. Roadside surface management technologies have vastly contributed to improved erosion control. Road construction often requires the travel surfaces to be lower than the surrounding landscape, leaving roadside slopes that require careful erosion management. Their research has shown that planting indigenous grass on composted surfaces is the quickest way to stabilize and increase soil's shear strength.

Soil Compaction

Sometimes life requires us to reach deep into our inner reserves for endurance, stamina, forgiveness, and resilience. Plants, too, need to go deep into the soil to be more drought resilient. Deep roots give the plant access to a broader spectrum of nutrients and better bind the ground for improved erosion prevention. Subsurface compaction, in people, causes a shallowness in character. In plants, it limits the roots to the top few inches of soil, leading to early seedling mortality. Soil compaction is measured in bulk density – the mass per volume ratio.

Soil with a higher bulk density is more densely packed. As the pore space in the soil is reduced, the weight of a given volume of soil increases. Plant root depth can be predicted by the soil's density values. Soil strength and loss of macro-porosity are just as crucial as bulk density.

The soil's tensile strength can be gauged using the flag test. Roots are most restricted by compaction when the soil is dry. Because of the compacted subsurface layers, less space is available for root development, air availability, and water penetration.

The solution is increased soil organic matter and soil biota (i.e., compost) – no surprise there. Increased soil organic matter can also be achieved by incorporating deep-root cover crops. During a regular freezing and thawing cycle, compacted soil fractures. Therefore, breaking compaction up is best done in early spring by adding compost to the affected area. Irrigate the site to provide soil biota an opportunity to penetrate deeper into the freshly fractured subsurface compacted layers. Their presence there will heal the ground, balance pH, develop aggregates and improve porosity.

Some compaction tests include using a section of wire. If, using only your hands, you cannot push the wire into the ground for at least 18 inches after a good rainfall, you need to take the remedial steps detailed in the above paragraph.

Water Infiltration, Drainage, and Holding Capacity

After heavy rain, water infiltrates into the soil, causing it to become saturated. The porosity of the ground is an essential factor in water infiltration. Soil water movement and retention are determined by the number, length, and diameter of pores. Most of the soil flow is caused by large pores (diameter greater than 1/16 inch). When it comes to water infiltration, texture and slope play a role. Sandy soils tend to be more efficient than siltier or clay soils. Generally speaking, water drains more quickly from higher points in the landscape. Water infiltration is governed mainly by the structure of the ground. The clay particles that clog pores are caused by unstable soil aggregates that disintegrate and dissolve in water. When soil is compacted, water cannot reach deeper subsoil layers where it can be stored for use by plants.

Soil permeability refers to the ability of water or air to pass through the soil. Pore size, shape, and density are all factors that determine how permeable a given soil is. Soil surveys have traditionally referred to permeability as saturated hydraulic conductivity.

Available water refers to soil water that can be accessed by plant roots and extracted from soil pores. This water resists evaporation and percolation due to suction forces within soil pores (cation-exchange capacity). Still, it is not so tightly held that roots cannot absorb it. The amount of water available to plants is known as the available water capacity (AWC).

Soil organic matter content can be improved, but soil texture still plays a significant role in water-holding capacity. By adding compost to the soil, soil water availability can be enhanced by reducing compaction and increasing the cation-exchange capacity (CEC). Any management strategy to raise infiltration and increase soil water storage by increasing the stability and number of fine aggregates is likely to be successful – this is a function of compost.

Soil Biodiversity

An abundance of life can thrive in the soil's complex ecosystem. Organic residue degradation and nutrient cycling in soil are made possible by a variety of soil life forms. The ground may include a wide range of organisms. If this is the case, plant growth will have a better chance of accessing nutrients. Pests and diseases can also be suppressed by the diversity and abundance of soil organisms.

In Chapter 3, we will delve into the different organisms in the soil biota – just an introduction. At the back of the book, we'll take an in-depth look at the full diversity and function within the soil food web. An indicator of active soil biota is the presence of earthworms. As a "keystone" participant in the soil food web, earthworms are vital.

The soil is home to a variety of earthworm species. Deep burrows are made by some species, while shallow holes are made by others. The passageways created by the movement of earthworms through the ground improve aeration and water infiltration and lubricate soil particles. Meanwhile, large amounts of organic and mineral soil are ingested and excreted as casts on the soil surface in some burrowing forms. More plant nutrients are available in casts of earthworms than in the surrounding soil. Their excrement aids in the stability of aggregates. In no-till systems, the soil mixing those earthworms provide is essential for nutrient cycling and the decomposition of organic matter.

Gardeners have a direct impact on soil microbial populations. Diversity and abundance of soil life may be improved by using crop residues or cover crops. Conversely, larger species are culled by the indiscriminate use of pesticides in the simazine, triazine, and carbamate groups. Anhydrous ammonia fertilizers also negatively affect soil biota. Tillage is necessary to incorporate organic residues, but soil organisms' habitats can be disrupted due to tilling. Earthworm populations can be harmed if surface residue, which provides food and protection, is removed.

Soil biodiversity is a direct product of compost and mulching. Sometimes it's the small things that matter. In gardening, it's the creatures so small they're invisible to the naked eye – microorganisms. Composting is the fastest, cheapest, most effective microorganism farming method. Farming and introducing microorganisms into your soil is the best possible soil health improvement measure you can take.

Plant and Root Growth

The health of individual plants in the field is a good indicator of plant vigor. Plant vigor is indicated by the uniformity of growth displayed by all crop plants in each lot. Healthy soil increases germination rates, reduces seedling mortalities, ensures uniformity in development, and is the basis for better yields. The root system is essential to the plant's growth and development.

While photosynthesis is an essential part of a plant's food conversion process, building blocks are absorbed via the roots in the form of inorganic ions. The roots of

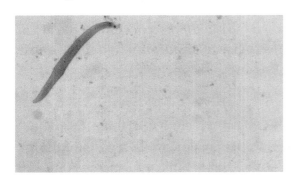

healthy plants can be as extensive as the plant's above-ground growth. For that to be possible, soil structure and vitality are essential. Root system development can be hindered by compacted subsoil layers that reduce the effective root zone. The system is paradoxically both robust and delicate. The robustness of soil is a factor of the diversity of the microorganism population. The system cannot control the proliferation of harmful bacteria, fungi, and nematodes in the absence of variety. Good soil structure is linked to a diverse range of soil organisms.

While healthy plants are an indicator of healthy soil, unhealthy plants can result from poor care of the plants themselves (late planting, insufficient irrigation or rainfall, etc.). It's critical to determine if the disease problem is linked to soil quality. Poor drainage (a sign of poor soil quality) may contribute to root-borne diseases. Growing healthy roots is easier with improved soil structure. Root growth can be inhibited by cultivating and compacting the soil. Healthy roots are an indication of a plant's overall health and vitality.

Healthy Soil's Response to pH

Acidity and alkalinity are indicated in pH, a scale between 0 and 14. The scale is logarithmic, meaning that pH 5.0 is 10 times more acid than soil with a pH reading of 6.0. A pH of 7.0 is neutral, 0 is most acidic, and 14 is purely alkaline. pH has a significant impact on plant nutrition, which has a direct effect on plant growth.

Plant nutrient release by weathering, soil solubility, and cation-exchange capacity (CEC) are all influenced by the pH of a soil's environment. As a result, the pH level is an excellent indicator of plant nutrient deficiencies. At pH values between 5.8 and 7.5, the availability of all plant nutrients is generally adequate. Neutral and alkaline soils have pH values between 6.66 and 7.33, while acidic soils have values below 6.66. The primary benefit of soil pH is the information it provides about the soil's other properties. CEC values, nutrient availability, and the release of toxic aluminum are all associated with pH.

Adding lime to acidic soils is a quick and straightforward way to raise the pH. (Dolomitic limestone is typically used). The pH of the top inch or two of a field that isn't tillage-intensive needs to be closely monitored because it can change very quickly. Most crops prefer a pH of 5.8 to 6.5. Inactivation of some herbicides can occur at a pH lower than 5.8. Toxicity to plants can be caused by the release of aluminum and manganese at acidities of 5.2.

Acidity (or alkalinity) can be reduced by organic matter. Organic matter decomposes into humus, which has molecules that can absorb or release hydrogen ions depending on the surrounding soil's pH. As a result, the soil's pH is kept stable by this buffering effect. Organic matter also decomposes and competes for aluminum ions ($Al+$) in solution, reducing its toxicity to plants.

Nutrient Holding Capacity of Healthy Soil

Gardeners view nutrient holding capacity as a process in which the soil acts as both a sink and a source of nutrients. The storage capacity, the rate of release, and the ability of the soil to replenish itself and provide nutrients to subsequent crops are essential considerations for gardeners and farmers.

Cation-exchange capacity (CEC) refers to the net surface charge of soil materials that enable them to hold and retain positively charged ionic nutrients against leaching. While both negative and positive charges are present, negative charges usually dominate.

Increasing the pH of the soil solution or adding compost increases the CEC. Examples of positively charged (cations) are:

- Potassium ($K+$)
- Ammonium (NH_4+)
- Calcium ($Ca2+$)
- Magnesium ($Mg2+$)
- Aluminum ($Al3+$)

Negatively charged ions (anions) are not attracted to negative surface charges and thus are more subject to leaching. Examples include:

- Nitrate (N03-)
- Chloride (Cl-)
- Sulfate (S04-)
- Phosphate (H2P04-)

Phosphate and sulfate are not leached as readily as nitrate, particularly in soils with iron-coated clays. Phosphate is also less mobile in soils because it is not soluble and binds readily with clays. Factors critical to nutrient holding capacity are pH, amount and kind of organic matter, soil texture, and clay type.

Soil test results will help predict whether the soil will provide nutrients fast enough to meet the crop's future needs. Currently, soil tests are most reliable for N, P, K, and Mg. While soils can be tested for other nutrients, interpretations are much less reliable. Soil tests can be valuable over the long run as they can show which soils are building nutrient levels and which ones are dropping.

Applications of high levels of fertilizers can skew test results. While heavy fertilization can lead to short-term increased productivity, it can also lead to leaching and nutrient loss. This approach also does little to improve other aspects of the soil, such as tilth or infiltration. Nutrient holding capacity is best enhanced by increasing soil organic matter, which serves as both a sink and a source for plant nutrients. Organic matter also extends the release of nutrients over a longer period.

Adding compost to your soil improves its CEC and a range of other soil-health indicators. Suppose high nutrient sources of organic matter such as animal manures are used. In that case, it is vital to know the nutrient values, particularly of N and P, before application so as not to over-apply the material and cause leaching or build-up of excess nutrients.

WARNING WITH REGARDS TO USING MANURES AND LAWN CLIPPINGS
It's important to note that adding manure to compost has some risks. Feedstock farmers sometimes use herbicides to maximize the feeding value of their crops. Some of these pesticides have active ingredients that aren't destroyed by thermophilic organisms or heat. Aminopyralid and clopyralid are examples of broadleaf pesticides that can remain latent in compost and subsequently be poisonous to plants. Avoid using manure of stock

that has been fed off treated lands. If you use Clopyralid on your lawn, the clippings are unsuitable for composting for the same reason.

Concerns arise when broiler litter is used as a feedstock for compost production. Commercial broiler operations use arsenic as a component of some feed medications or growth promoters, but the FDA has recently restricted their use in poultry operations. Poultry incorporate much of the arsenic they consume into their excrement and litter, which increases the risk of arsenic leaching from compost piles into lakes and streams.

BENEFICIAL IMPACT ON VEGETATION

Photosynthesis is one of nature's miracles. Photon cells of different sizes allow some plants to thrive in the shade while others need full sun. Plants, taking up chemical elements in inorganic ion form, use the sun's energy to manufacture their own food, combining the chemical elements into many organic compounds. Essentially, photosynthesis is a chemical process in which light energy is captured and mixed with carbon dioxide and water to make sugars used as a chemical energy source.

$6 \times CO_2$ (carbon dioxide molecules) add $12 \times H_2O$ (water molecules). The photosynthesis cell using sunlight produces $C_6H_{12}O_6$ (sugars), $6 \times H_2O$ (water), and $6 \times O_2$ (oxygen)

Plants require 17 nutrients to thrive and cannot complete their life cycles if any of these 17 elements are missing. Cells and enzymes are made up of compounds of these nutrients. It's one of nature's wonders that takes place all around us every day. Some of the plant's chemical processes cannot take place without the assistance of microorganisms.

The 17 Essential Plant Nutrients

Sourced from Water

Carbon (C)
Oxygen (O)

Sourced from the Air

Hydrogen (H)
Oxygen (O)

Sourced from the Soil

Primary Nutrients	*Secondary Nutrients*	*Micronutrients*	
Nitrogen (N)	Calcium (Ca)	Boron (B)	Manganese (Mn)
Phosphorous (P)	Magnesium (Mg)	Chrorine (Cl)	Molybdenum (Mo)
Potassium (K)	Sulfur (S)	Copper (Cu)	Zinc (Zn)
		Iron (Fe)	Nickel (N)

Through carbon dioxide and water, plants receive the necessary nutrients and, using light, manufacture their food. Most plants are composed primarily (95%) of these three nutrients – carbon, oxygen, and hydrogen. The remaining 14 elements make up the remaining 5% of the plant's dry matter. A deficiency in one or more of these 14 essential elements may impede the plant's growth ability. The 17 elements are crucial, but others are also ingested by plants, though their purpose is uncertain.

Plants primarily ingest these elements from the soil's solution. According to the amount of nutrients plants need and the extent of deficiency, the 14 mineral nutrients are categorized as primary, secondary, or micronutrients. Deficiencies in primary nutrients are often the first to show up in the soil, as they are used the most. A macronutrient is a term used to describe primary and secondary nutrients. Unlike primary nutrients, secondary nutrients are more rarely deficient in soils. Micronutrients (also known as trace or minor elements) are required in much smaller quantities and are less frequently deficient soil. Nutrients are used in varying amounts, but each one is just as critical to the growth of plants. Below is a list of the 17 essential plant nutrients.

Electrically charged ions are the natural form in which all chemical elements, including plant nutrients, exist. Ions are either positively or negatively charged. Ions with a positive charge are called cations (the C reminds me it's charged). Ions with a negative charge are called anions. Plants can only use nutrients in their ionic form. Still, some nutrients can be used by plants in more than one ionic form simultaneously. The following is a list of some of the most common soil cations and anions.

CATIONIC NUTRIENTS

- K+   Potassium   Primary Nutrient
- NH4+   Ammonium   Primary Nutrient (Nitrogen)
- Mg+2   Magnesium   Secondary Nutrient
- Ca+2   Calcium   Secondary Nutrient
- Mn+2   Manganese   Trace Element
- Zn+2   Zinc   Trace element

ANIONIC NUTRIENTS

- NO3-   Nitrate   Primary Element (Nitrogen)
- SO4-2   Sulfate   Secondary Nutrient (Sulfur)
- H2PO4-   Dihydrogen Phosphate   Primary Nutrient (Phosphorous)
- HPO4-2   Hydrogen phosphate   Primary Nutrient (Phosphorous)
- Cl-   Chloride   Trace Element (Chlorine)
- BO3-2   Borate   Trace Element (Boron)
- MoO3-2   Molybdenum Trioxide   Trace Element (Molybdenum)

CATIONIC NON-NUTRIENTS

- Na+   Sodium
- H+   Hydrogen‡
- Al+3   Aluminum

ANIONIC NON-NUTRIENTS

- OH-   Hydroxyl
- H2CO3-   Bicarbonate
- CO3-3   Carbonate

‡ *Plants get their supply of hydrogen from water through photosynthesis. Excess hydrogen ions in soil impact pH, which affects several chemical and biological processes.*

THE ROLE OF ORGANIC MATTER IN PLANT HEALTH

We've seen the benefits of compost to soil health, but how does that affect plant health? Above are the basics of a plant's dietary requirements, the digestive system of plants, and the role of CEC in the food supply. Compost is an essential part of the nutrient supply chain for plants:

- Soil structure is improved. Soil aggregates are held together by organic matter, which acts as glue. Aggregates are less stable and more easily broken apart when they are devoid of organic matter. Water flow and root penetration are improved, while soil crusting, clod formation, and erosion are minimized with good soil structure – a product of compost.

- Cations can be attracted and held by organic matter in the soil.

- Compost provides and microorganisms deliver plant nutrients. Soil fertility is one of the organic matter's most critical functions.

  o Compost can supply as much as 98% of a plant's nitrogen and sulfur requirements and up to 50% of their phosphorous needs.

  o Approximately 5% of soil organic matter is nitrogen and 0.5% sulfur or potash.

  o Most micronutrients can be found in their available forms in organic matter, which serves as their primary storage location.

  o Unlike other elements, potassium is not found in organic form. The humus-producing microorganisms release ionic nutrients that plants can use, even though the organic matter cannot.

Soil organic matter cannot be rapidly increased. A 6-inch-deep acre of soil contains approximately 2,000,000 pounds of dirt. About 20,000 pounds of stable humus are needed to raise this layer's organic matter content by one percentage point (2,000,000 x 0.01). About two-thirds of the carbon in crop residues is released as carbon dioxide during decomposition, leaving only a fraction of the added carbon to become stable humus. As a result, adding crop residues to the soil to increase its organic matter content can take longer. Increasing soil organic matter without adding compost requires reducing or eliminating tillage operations, controlling soil erosion, and producing high crop yields, including winter cover crops. The purpose of legume winter cover crops would be to incorporate them into the soil to add organic matter.

Consider CEC once more. In the composting process, particles are formed that have a net negative electrical charge. Like how opposite poles of a magnet attract each other, these charges attract and hold the opposite (positive) charges. Negatively charged colloids, (a homogeneous noncrystalline substance consisting of large molecules or ultramicroscopic particles of one substance dispersed through a second substance) like poles of a magnet, repel each other in the same way. Cations can also be attracted and held by negatively charged soil particles because of the attraction of opposite charges. However, the soil colloids (clay and humus) hold cations in place but not in a non-resistant way to leaching. These cations, however, may be released into the soil solution and absorbed by plant roots through an exchange process. The negative charges on the surface of the colloids are known as exchange sites because they allow one cation to exchange for another. One of the most important soil properties for soil fertility and plant nutrition is the soil's ability to attract and hold positively charged nutrients. Known as CEC.

There is a wide range of milliequivalent capacity per 100 grams of clay, from 3 to nearly 100mE. Soils with a cation exchange capacity of 10 to 20mE/100 gm of soil or higher are ideal for plant-nutrient relationships. Compost is charged to the maximum (100 – 200mE). The exchange capacity of organic matter is extremely high. Therefore, it is useful as a source of nutrients, a soil structure enhancer, and a water reservoir.

Hydrogen ($H+$), ammonium, potassium, sodium, calcium, zinc, magnesium, and other cations react with the compost and are held loosely enough for plant roots to access them (e.g., $Na+$, $K+$). Negatively charged anions like sulfates ($O4S-2$), nitrates ($NO3-$), and hydroxyl ($OH-$) are repelled by compost. Anions cannot be held by compost. In soil, soluble anions move with the water supply and are prone to leaching if not absorbed by the plant.

Cations that are more tightly held than others are more likely to be replaced on an exchange site than those more loosely held. Even $Na+$, however, can take the place of $H+$. Exchange is also affected by the ratio of one nutrient to another. For example, $K+$ ions have a greater chance of replacing a more tightly bonded cation when potassium fertilizer is used at an exchange site.

Only a small percentage of soil colloids are positively charged. Because anions have negative electrical charges, soil colloids cannot hold on to them. Several anions are water-soluble and move with the water, such as nitrate, sulfate, and chloride. With low pH conditions, positive charges on the organic matter can hold sulfate in a loosely bound state.

The "law of limiting factors" is a critical principle in plant nutrition. This law states that the factor with the shortest supply limits yields or plant growth. The most limiting growth factor or nutrient – it may be water – also limits output. Although this law applies to nutrients and other factors that affect growth, it is also applicable to management variables. The use of high rates of compost on crops is pointless if weeds, insects, and diseases are not controlled or unsuitable varieties are planted.

Through their roots, plants obtain nutrients and water from the soil. If soil conditions such as moisture, air, nutrients, temperature, soluble salts, and tilth are favorable, plant roots will continue to grow. Root growth will be restricted if there are unfavorable conditions. Soil compaction, excess water, and dry soil are the three most common root-growth-inhibiting factors. In dry soil, roots cannot grow.

COMPOST AS A SUSTAINABILITY FACTOR

Estimations are that in the next 40 years, we will need to produce as much food (calories) as was grown in the 10,000 preceding years combined. For humanity to survive and prosper, we must have healthy soil. While we may imagine that hydroponics is a feasible alternative, 95% of all food consumed is grown in soil.

When farmers still used mules or oxen to pull plows to cultivate their land, the damage caused to soil was limited. In 1917, Henry Ford started mass-producing the Fordson tractor. My granddad owned a Fordson Major that still required you to crank it with a sling to get it started. I would sit on it, my foot on the brake as my Gramps cranked away in front, sweat pouring off him – not always in the cheeriest of moods, as I recall. Survivors that remember the 1930s Dust Bowl will now be centenarians – I expect there are but a handful. The picture shows devastating scenes caused by four successive seasons of drought (and unwise tillage practices made possible by tractors). Ruined lands and ruined families thrown into abject poverty. Hindsight has the privilege of 20/20 vision.

Below is a quote from the Monthly Weather Review of June 1936[2]:

> *The occupation of this Great Plains area for agricultural purposes began about 1885, when there was a migration of land seekers into the region. The settlers made their livelihood by crop farming, at which they succeeded well for 3 or 4 years. Then came 3 "lean years"; 1894 was a year of complete crop failure, due to drought. In some parts of the plain's region as many as 90 percent of the settlers left their farms. Following this recession in land settlement, a gradual healing-over of the denuded fields by native grama-buffalo sod took place. The settlers who remained learned from experience how to cope more effectively with the unfavorable crop years and with drought. The next impetus to land settlement and crop farming was given by the high prices offered for agricultural products during and immediately following the World War. Promoters launched campaigns to get crop farmers instead of cattle raisers interested in the region, tractors and other labor-saving machinery were introduced, and grain farming was undertaken on a rather large scale. Reckless denuding by cultivation and overgrazing continued this land, where rainfall at best is light.*

The dust storms that ravaged the Great Plains in the 1930s were caused by a combination of dry weather and poor soil conservation practices. Even in Washington, D.C., the sun was obscured by dust from the Great Plains. Congress heard testimony from President Roosevelt's advisor, Hugh Hammond Bennett, on the need for improved soil conservation techniques in March 1935. "This, gentlemen, is what I've been talking about," Mr. Bennett said, pointing to the evidence in the window. Before the year ended, Congress passed the Soil Conservation Act.

The adage "seeing is believing" worked to Mr. Bennet's advantage. Regrettably, it was only with the advent of the phase-contrast microscope, invented by Frita Zernike in 1932, that colorless and transparent biological materials could be studied. Finally! We could see what really matters, though we hardly understood their critical function in *actual* soil conservation.

---

2   *mwr-193506.pdf (weather.gov)*

If history has taught us anything, it's that the media has an untoward influence. Often, that influence is for the benefit of the few at the expense of the many. The continued normalization of the use of plows and synthetic fertilizer is an example. Backed by vast resources, both financial and political advocates, the belief that the ground should be plowed and fertilized is accepted as standard practice. The result is that humans have drastically transformed Earth's protective soil layers, with agriculture and mining being among the most damaging land uses.

Disturbing the surface soil interferes with delicately balanced systems. Well-established interactions among plant roots, fungi, bacteria, micro-, and macrofauna are destroyed once vegetation is removed and soil is upturned, buried, or eroded away. Functional microbial-root networks need to be brought back effectively to remediate soil vitality to improve soil structure, nutrient recycling, water retention, and plant productivity.

Compost, or the cultivation and proliferation of microorganisms, is central to our survival. There is nothing more central to life on earth than microorganisms – and composting is one of the most effective ways to increase their soil population.

3. SOIL FOOD WEB INTRODUCTION

INTRODUCTION

In reviewing what compost is and its crucial role in developing healthy soil, we regularly referred to microorganisms, soil biota, and the soil food web. Some of the words are interchangeable, depending on the context in which they are used: Allow me to create some order by clarifying and layering the different terms.

BIG PICTURE (MACRO-ENVIRONMENT)

Gardeners use the outermost layer of the earth to grow plants, referred to as the pedosphere. The pedosphere (what we walk on) interacts with and is influenced by other spheres:

- **Atmosphere** – referring to the air above the earth. The atmosphere provides the pedosphere with energy. There's an interchange of gasses between the pedosphere and the atmosphere. The atmosphere also has a precipitation/evaporation relationship with the hydrosphere and a respiration/photosynthesis relationship with the biosphere.

- **Biosphere** – referring to life on earth. The biosphere's life (and death) directly impacts the pedosphere. The pedosphere recycles elements and sustains life within and on itself.

- **Lithosphere** – referring to the substrata below the pedosphere. The lithosphere influences the pedosphere's composition. The lithosphere is altered by the activity of living organisms and plants in the pedosphere. Leaching from the pedosphere also changes the lithosphere.

- **Hydrosphere** – referring to the earth's water. The hydrosphere interacts with the pedosphere through precipitation and groundwater, and it alters the lithosphere in freeze/thaw cycles.

THE ENVIRONMENT OF YOUR YARD/PLOT (MESO-ENVIRONMENT)

Depending on the size of your available gardening soil, local environments affect each other. An example is trench composting. While organisms in the micro-environment actively decompose the buried fresh organic matter, the surrounding soil benefits. More on this later.

Below is an inexhaustive list of meso-environment management considerations:

- Soil erosion management
- Landscaping
- Complementing plants
- Organic pest management
- Organic disease management
- Plant choices and vegetation cycling

THE MICRO-ENVIRONMENT

By micro, I mean itsy bitsy small. This is where billions of the microorganisms we're interested in live and have a massive influence. This micro-environment comprises biota (fauna and flora), minerals, organic material, non-organic materials, water, and air. The interaction between the different biota is called the **soil food web**.

THE SOIL BIOTA INTERACTIONS

A biological *universe* exists in a mere cup of soil from the pedosphere. There are millions of species in soil biota, yet only a fraction has been identified. This chapter explores how soil biota transforms energy, builds its environment, and plays a critical role in the earth's sustainability.

The soil's food web is a highly dynamic, complex environment. The living part of the soil is very complex, interchanging, and in constant flux. One could write an epic novel (or create a reality show) on biota interactions in the soil food web. It's all high drama of who ate whom, the transactions between the rhizobium consortium and leguminous roots, odd communities, and weird couples. While I joke, this is the stuff that is vital to life on earth. It's these biota communities that enable us to breathe, eat, remain healthy, break down pathogens, and produce the antibiotics we take to fight infections – and much more. Soil biota is responsible for mineralization, decomposition, fixation, immobilization, respiration, and other processes. These processes support growth and transformation in the pedosphere, biosphere, atmosphere, hydrosphere, and lithosphere – everywhere.

BIOLOGICAL INTERACTION

Let's reverse-engineer – starting at the point when your compost has been made and added to the soil. And fascinatingly, with little surprise – on the center stage is organic matter: compost. Stable compost and organic material in the composting process fuels the exchanges in the soil food web. Without these two processes you're learning about, there would be no microorganisms to fuel the plant with essential nutrients. Soil organic matter is the nutritional storehouse for plants and soil microorganisms.

Carbon's presence provides bacteria, fungi, and actinomycetes (and minor role actors) with an energy source and makes up half of their cell mass. Nitrogen's role is to provide microorganisms and soil fauna the proteins, amino acids, nucleic acids, enzymes, and co-enzymes required to grow and function. The primary consumers (organisms that eat the organic residues) utilize about 333% more carbon than nitrogen in the composting process. A compost pile that starts out with a 30:1 C:N ratio will have a 10:1 ratio by the end of the aerobic process.

Some of the carbon consumption is mineralized, and the rest is sequestrated as carbon dioxide. The consumed nitrogen is captured in the cell of the organisms. The demise and consumption of the first-tier microorganisms (bacteria, fungi, actinomycetes, protozoa, archaea, and algae) by second-tier soil animals (protozoa, nematodes, mites, springtails, spiders, insects, and earthworms) releases the consumed nitrogen and other minerals into the soil, available to plants in ionic form.

SOIL FOOD WEB

ORGANIC MATTER TURNOVER

Microflora consume carbon-rich materials (often called brown materials) and nitrogen-rich (green) materials. Active microflora can roughly be grouped as fungi and bacteria. Mycorrhizae (symbiotic root fungi) and actinomycetes (stuck somewhere between fungi and bacteria, as I understand it) deserve a special mention. This is the team responsible for decomposing organic matter. PS: Actinomycetes are essential microflora that live in your mouth and gut and help you keep healthy. They are also responsible for that lovely earthy smell of compost.

NUTRIENT TRANSFER FUNCTION

Microfauna consume the microflora above. These are bacteria-feeding nematodes and protozoa. Fungal-feeding protozoa feed on mycorrhizae. Fungal-feeding nematodes eat fungi and fungi-feeding protozoa. Yum.

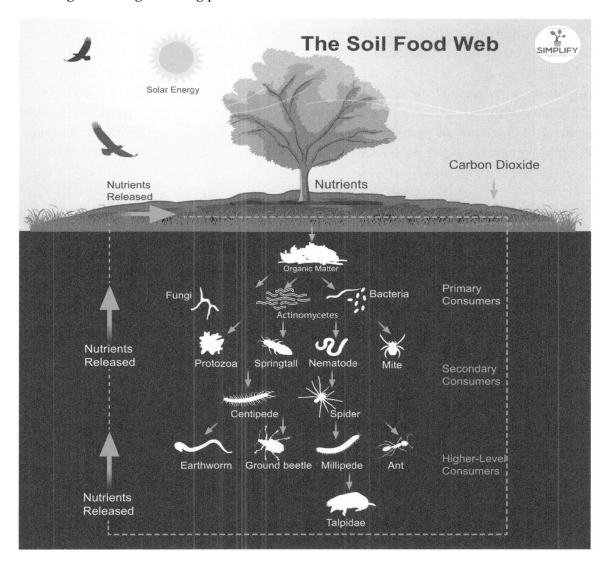

SOIL STRUCTURE IMPROVERS

Mesofauna collembola (small wingless anthropods – springtails, mites) graze on mycelium (fungal and bacterial). These also feed on the bacteria-eating nematodes. In the process, they contribute to both soil structure improvement and disease transmission and prevention.

POLLUTANT DEGRADATION

Macrofauna are responsible for disease transmission and prevention as well. Their role includes degrading pollutants. Enchytraeids (pot worms) consume springtails and mites that, in turn, have fed on bacteria eating nematodes. Enchytraeidae are responsible for creating aggregates as a result of their fecal pellets and through burrowing activities. They have high resistance to toxic environments and can heal degraded soils, such as mining sites.

Macroarthropods are capable of restructuring soil profiles. These are the ecosystem engineers – the ants and termites. Spiders and centipedes are also included in this group, and earthworms part of the macrofauna group too. They are an essential part of the biota and are often used as an indicator of soil health.

ACTIVE MICROORGANISMS IN AEROBIC COMPOSTING

In the previous section, we explored flora and fauna active in the pedosphere after adding compost. In this section, we'll look at the host of microorganisms responsible for producing aerobic compost. We will explore the different types of composting and the organisms involved in each process in Chapter 5. The function of organisms in the hot-and-fast aerobic process (the one we're looking at) is to break down organic matter. In the process, they produce heat, release carbon dioxide and water, and, of course, manufacture humus.

In compost production using the hot process (aerobic), the pile goes through three stages. Each stage has a set of microorganisms that likes (or can survive) the temperatures they're responsible for. It's a case of if the kitchen gets too hot for you, get out. The three stages are referred to as mesophilic, thermophilic, and psychrophilic. Each of these stages is primarily indicated by the temperatures caused by the different organisms.

Aerobic composting has two distinct phases: (1) the active composting phase and (2) the curing phase. As active composting is accelerated by organisms consuming readily available degradable material, things heat up from 50 degrees Fahrenheit to 105 degrees Fahrenheit. The initial decomposers are mesophilic bacteria, fungi (responsible for decomposing more resistant materials), and actinomycetes.

The rising temperature, caused by energy released by the active mesophilic microorganisms, pushes the process into the thermophilic stage (from 105 degrees

Fahrenheit to as high as 170 degrees Fahrenheit). It is in the thermophilic stage that pathogens and weed seeds are destroyed. Some organisms die in the high heat, some become dormant, and some remain productive, though less active.

During the curing phase, the microbial activity is less intense until the humus is fully stabilized. Stabilization occurs when the compost reaches its final curing stage. As the composting process progresses, the temperatures in a pile fluctuate quite a bit. Depending on the temperature, some microorganisms will have an easier time surviving, while others may perish.

THE AEROBIC COMPOSTING PROCESS

As a general rule, temperatures below 50 degrees Fahrenheit are considered to be psychrophilic. In a mesophilic environment, the transitional temperature ranges from 50 degrees Fahrenheit to 105 degrees Fahrenheit. At 105 degrees Fahrenheit and above, the thermophilic organisms thrive. No matter how you define these temperature ranges, microorganisms that thrive in a pile during the mesophilic stage may also survive in the psychrophilic and thermophilic phases. These ranges represent the point at which certain types of microorganisms reach their maximum growth and productivity.

As the microbial population grows and diversifies, the temperature rises steadily through the psychrophilic and mesophilic temperature ranges. Heat is rapidly generated by microbial activity and their population expansion as they break down highly available degradable material. The temperature of the compost pile builds up from the self-insulated center.

The thermophilic stage typically takes two to three days to reach its peak in the compost pile, depending on several factors. With temperatures in the thermophilic zone, the pile becomes populated by microbes at their most efficient and productive levels. Pathogens, fly larvae, and weed seeds are destroyed by the high levels of microbial activity and the accompanying high temperatures.

Because of the microorganism diversity, complex and decay-resistant materials, such as cellulose and lignins, are more quickly and efficiently degraded. Temperatures can quickly reach 130 to 160 degrees Fahrenheit. As available degradable material and oxygen decrease, so does the microbial activity.

At high temperatures, enzymes responsible for the breakdown of the material denature and become ineffective, preventing microorganisms from obtaining the nutrition they need to survive. Even though some organisms may withstand high temperatures, they may be less efficient and active. Another way that microorganisms respond to heat stress is by producing spores. Some microorganisms take the inactive form of spores to protect themselves from conditions detrimental to their survival, such as heat and dehydration. Once more favorable conditions are present, the spores begin to germinate.

As microbial activity decreases, the pile starts cooling. Different microorganisms return to the pile as the temperature cools from thermophilic levels, and spores germinate as the conditions become more favorable for survival. Decomposition is further aided by these microorganisms. The compost pile can remain in the thermophilic range for 10 to 60 days, depending on the method of operation.

Curing or reactivation of active composting can begin once temperatures fall below 105 degrees Fahrenheit. There is no fixed point at which active composting is considered finished. Still, continuous cycles of reheating with lower peaks are an indicator that the pile is stabilizing. When the pile conditions are such that microbial activity cannot rise high enough to reheat the pile, it is considered finished.

Curing is an essential part of the composting process, even though microbial activity is lower and most organic material has already been degraded. A lower level of microbial activity characterizes curing, which stabilizes the products of active composting. It includes the further decomposition of organic acids and decay-resistant substances, humic compounds and nitrate-nitrogen formation, and stabilization. Some fungi can begin to grow in a batch during curing and help improve the compost's disease-fighting properties.

When pile temperatures remain low due to the decreased microbial activity and lower levels of heat generation it is important to control moisture levels. During the curing period, proper moisture and oxygen management are still necessary to maintain microbial activity. It is also essential at this point to ensure that the batch isn't contaminated with weed seeds. Curing can be a time-consuming process. A more extended curing period is needed if the compost is to be used for sensitive purposes like planting media. As soon as the pile cools down to room temperature, it's considered to have finished curing – not to be confused with an end of the process caused by a lack of oxygen or moisture.

AEROBIC DECOMPOSERS

BACTERIA

The bacteria commonly found in compost piles are aerobic bacteria, and they specialize in breaking down organic compounds and thrive at temperatures of up to 170 degrees Fahrenheit (77 degrees Celsius). Bacterial populations vary from pile to pile depending on various factors, including the compost's raw materials, heat level, air volume, moisture content, and the pile's geographic location. Microorganisms, such as bacteria, are single-celled organisms that can take on various shapes and sizes. It would take 25,000 bacteria laid end-to-end to fill an inch on a ruler, and a pea-sized amount of garden soil may contain up to a billion bacteria. Unlike more complex green plants, Bacteria are colorless and unable to produce carbohydrates from sunlight, water, and carbon dioxide. Bacteria can be either free-living or colonial.

Binary fission is how all organisms reproduce. In this process, the nucleus splits in two, and a new cell wall grows across the middle of the cell. There are two nuclei in each half of the cell, which creates a unique individual.

A colony of bacteria can multiply into billions in just a few days if the conditions are ideal. One generation of bacteria lives for about 20 to 30 minutes, so a single cell can produce billions of offspring in a matter of hours.

Among all organisms, bacteria are the most diverse in their ability to eat a wide variety of foods. The most common type found in compost piles is heterotrophic bacteria, and they can feed on both living and dead organic matter. Usually, bacteria can synthesize the enzymes they need to break down whatever material they come across. Aerobic respiration, which compost bacteria use as an energy source, is made possible by respiratory enzymes in the cell membrane.

It is difficult for bacteria to flee an unfavorable environment because of their small size, limited mobility, and lack of complexity. Bacteria can be rendered inactive or killed if the pile's temperature drops or its acidity changes suddenly. Bacteria that previously dominated a heap may be wiped out if the environment changes.

More than 80% to 90% of microorganisms in a gram of compost are made up of bacteria. Compost decomposition and heat generation are primarily driven by bacteria. Compost organisms that use a wide range of enzymes to break down many organic materials are the most nutrient-diverse.

A single-celled bacterium is either a bacillus, cocci, or a spiral, depending on the cell's shape. Many are motile, which means they can move on their own. During the first stages of composting, mesophilic bacteria are the most prevalent. The majority of these are topsoil-found organisms.

Thermophilic bacteria take over when the compost reaches temperatures above 40 degrees Celsius 104 degrees Fahrenheit. Bacillus species predominate in this phase's microbial populations. Bacilli species diversity is high between 50 and 55 degrees Celsius, 122 and 131 degrees Fahrenheit, but it plummets to almost nothing above 60 degrees Celsius, 140 degrees Fahrenheit. To survive in unfavorable environments, bacteria produce endospores, thick-walled spores that can withstand extremes of temperature, humidity, dryness, and lack of food. As long as the environment is right for them to do so, they are always present.

How did microorganisms that can withstand the high temperatures in active compost evolve in nature? Bacteria belonging to the Thermus genus have been found at the hottest compost temperatures. Thermus bacteria have been discovered in Yellowstone National Park's hot springs. Thermal conditions in nature can also be found in manure, sea thermal vents, and piles of decomposing vegetation that can heat up like a compost pile in the right conditions.

Mesophilic bacteria return to the compost as it cools down. Compost recolonization is dependent on the presence of mesophilic microbes and the surrounding environment. The more diverse the microbial community is the longer the curing or stabilization period.

FUNGAL LIFE

Bacteria are smaller than fungi, and they form filaments, which are strands of individual cells. It is common for fungi to be present in the final stages of composting because of the material they decompose. Waxes, proteins, hemicelluloses, lignin, and pectin are just a few of the decay-resistant materials that most fungi eat. Because most fungi are obligate aerobes (meaning they require oxygen to grow), they have a lower tolerance for low-oxygen environments than bacteria, which are less sensitive to low moisture and pH. Temperatures above 140 degrees Fahrenheit kill off fungi.

Above 140 degrees Fahrenheit is too hot for fungi to thrive. If piles exceed 140 degrees Fahrenheit, the composting process will not wholly decompose any resistant material.

So, while high temperatures are desirable for pathogen destruction, they must be regulated so that beneficial organisms are not destroyed and the decomposition process is not hindered.

ACTINOMYCETES

To give newly plowed soil its characteristic earthy scent, actinomycetes (a type of bacteria higher than fungi and molds) are responsible. Humidity is a product of humus formation, and actinomycetes play an essential role in this process. In contrast to most bacteria, actinomycetes can be found several feet down in the soil. They break down plant matter into a peat-like substance deep in the roots. Carbon, nitrogen, and ammonia are released into the atmosphere by actinomycetes as they decompose plant and animal matter. The majority are aerobic and mesophilic, and they can be found on any natural substrate. According to a study, actinomycetes make up at least 5% of the soil's bacterial population. Because actinomycetes can produce antibiotics that inhibit bacterial growth, their population needs to be limited. This is partly done by the thermophilic temperatures.

Actinomycetes, which resemble fungi but are actually filamentous bacteria, are responsible for the earthy smell of soil. Their multicellular filaments resemble those of fungi, but they lack nuclei. Cellulose, lignin, chitin, and proteins are complex organics that actinomycetes break down in composting. For example, their enzymes allow them to break down woody stems, bark, or newspaper.

In compost, long, branched filaments of actinomycetes can be seen as gray spider webs stretching through the soil. These filaments are most commonly found in the pile's final 10 to 15 centimeters when composting. Occasionally, they form circular colonies that grow in diameter over time.

PROTOZOA

One-celled microorganisms known as protozoa are found in water droplets in compost, but their role in decomposition is minimal. Although they feed on organic matter (similar to bacteria), protozoa also eat bacteria and fungi as part of their diet.

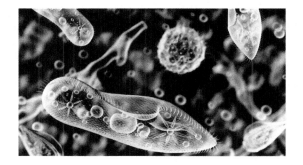

PHYSICAL DECOMPOSERS

Physical decomposers are the larger organisms that pulverize material as they eat through the compost pile. The organisms found in almost any compost pile are listed below. Due to their preference for moderate or moderately warm temperatures, these creatures will not be present at all times.

ROTIFERS
Rotifers are multicellular microorganisms that can be found in compost and water films. They consume organic matter, as well as bacteria and fungi.

MITES
Ticks, spiders, and horseshoe crabs all share a common ancestor with six appendages that resemble the mites legs. They can be both free-living and parasitic at the same time. As a general rule, a mite's length ranges from one-tenth of an inch to half an inch, depending on the species. Mites have a rapid life cycle, going from larva to nymph to adult to dormant in days. There are two types of second-level consumers: those that prey on plants and those that prey on other animals. Mites prey on the latter.

MILLIPEDES
The millipede's worm-like body has numerous leg-bearing segments, each with two pairs of walking legs aside from the front few. Eggs are laid in the soil in the spring and hatch into tiny worms, but little else is known about their life cycles. Millipedes molt several times before they reach adulthood. In their adult form, millipedes can grow up to 1 to 2 inches in length. They feed directly on plant material, which aids in decomposition.

CENTIPEDES
Segmented flatworms with up to 15 pairs of legs, each leg on a separate segment, are known as centipedes. Eggs are laid during the spring and summer months, and the chicks hatch and grow to adulthood. As third-level consumers, centipedes eat insects and spiders only – they are not omnivores.

SOWBUGS
Segments are clearly defined in the sowbug's fat, flat body. There are many structural similarities between this creature and the crayfish. An egg is laid by a sowbug, and when it hatches, it develops into a baby sowbug. Sowbugs may overrun a compost pile because the females can deposit a large number of eggs at once. They feed on decomposing vegetation, which makes them first-level consumers.

SNAILS AND SLUGS

Mollusks such as snails and slugs have muscular disks on the undersides of their bodies that enable them to creep. There are three distinct features of snails: their spirally curved shell, their wide retractable foot, and their distinct head. It is not uncommon to mistake one slug species for half of a potato because they are so similar in appearance. Eggs and larvae are laid in capsules or gelatinous masses. The snail or slug progresses through the various stages of life to become an adult. Plant material is the primary source of their nutrition. Still, they'll also eat fresh garbage and plant debris, which can be found in the compost. You should be on the lookout for them as you spread your compost, as they can cause damage to crops if they make their way into your garden.

SPIDERS

Arachnid-related spiders, also known as mites, are among the garden's least-liked inhabitants. These eight-legged creatures are third-level consumers of insects and small invertebrates. They can assist in controlling garden pests by feeding on these creatures.

SPRINGTAILS

Springtails are tiny insects measuring no more than a quarter of an inch in length at their widest point. In addition to their ability to jump, they can be found in various colors and patterns. They eat decaying plants, pollen, grains, and fungi.

BEETLES

The most common beetles found in compost are the rove beetle, the ground beetle, and the feather-winged beetle. These insects have two pairs of wings, the more forward-placed of which serve as a shield for the folded and thinner back-set ones that are used for flight. As second-level consumers, feather-winged beetles feed on fungal spores. In contrast, rove and ground beetles, which are larger, prey on other insects. Soft-shelled grubs that feed and grow during the warm months are beetles in their immature state. Mature grubs emerge from a resting or pupal stage when fully grown and become hard-bodied, winged adults. Insects, snails, and other small animals are prey for most adult beetles. Still, some, like the rove and ground beetles, prefer to eat decaying vegetation. Insects such as snails and slugs are well-known victims of the black rove beetle. When slugs become a problem in their gardens, some people bring them in from outside.

ANTS

Anthracnose honeydew, fungi, seeds, sugar, scraps, other insects, and even other ants are all food sources for ants. Some of these foods can be found in compost, as well as shelter for nests and hills. However, they will only remain as long as the pile is cool. In addition to consuming organic matter, ants bring fungi and other organisms into their nests, where they feed on the first-level consumers. Composter phosphorus and potassium levels can be improved through ant-mediated mineral transfer.

FLIES

In the larval stage, flies, such as the black fungus gnats and soldiers, spend their time in compost as maggots. As long as it's organic, adults can eat it. The life cycle includes four stages: egg, larva, pupa, and adult. The eggs are laid in a variety of organic matter. When a single housefly crawls across a sterile plate of lab gelatin, bacteria colonies appear in its tracks as they are very effective bacteria distributors. See how flying insects provide ideal airborne transportation for bacteria on their way to the compost pile during the early stages of composting?

Horseflies, mosquitoes, and houseflies will not be able to breed in your compost pile if you keep a layer of dry leaves or grass clippings on top and cover your garbage as soon as you finish building it. Due to its thermophilic temperatures, a well-managed compost pile is inhospitable to fly larvae. Frost kills most flies, but a few that survive can quickly repopulate a region before the warm season has even begun, even though most of them die.

WORMS

Compost contains various organisms, including nematodes (eelworms), free-living flatworms, and rotifers. It is possible to divide the microscopic organisms known as nematodes into three main groups: those that feed on decaying organic matter; those that prey on the other nematodes in the soil; those that attack the roots of plants; and those that can be pests in gardens. They are flatworms, as their name implies, and they're usually relatively small in their free-living incarnations. The majority of

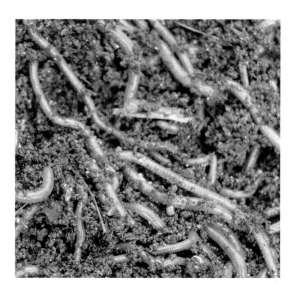

flatworms are carnivorous and live within the compost structure in a thin layer of water. There are many types of rotifers, which are multicellular animals that live in tubes attached to a pile of debris. They have three distinct parts: a head, a trunk, and a tail. It is common for them to be found in watery environments, and many of the species are aquatic. There are rotifers in compost that feed on microorganisms that adhere to plant matter in water.

EARTHWORMS

The heavyweight champ of microscopic decomposition is undoubtedly the earthworm. Since it was discovered that earthworms spend most of their time tilling and enriching the soil, they have been the subject of much admiration. According to Charles Darwin, a great English naturalist, all of our planet's fertile land has been tilled by earthworms at some point.

The alimentary canal ingests, decomposes, and deposits casts during the earthworm's active periods. Calciferous glands near the worm's gizzard break down and neutralize organic matter as it moves through the digestive system of an earthworm. Before digestion, food is finely ground in the gizzard. Hormones, enzymes, and other fermenting substances are found in digestive juices in the intestine. Casts are the richest and best quality of all humus material coming from a worm's body. Bacteria, organic matter, available nitrogen, calcium and magnesium, and available phosphorus and potassium are all significantly higher in fresh casts than in the soil.

In a well-managed compost pile, earthworms thrive, contributing to the compost's quality both physically and chemically. Taking advantage of earthworms' unique abilities in composting is a wise gardener's responsibility.

ANAEROBIC DECOMPOSERS

While aerobic composting is referred to as traditional composting, anaerobic composting has a definite place in managing organic waste. Chapter 6 reviews different anaerobic processes, including fermentation (Bokashi) and trench composting. Below is an introduction to the process and the bacteria and fungi responsible for the anaerobic composting.

FERMENTATION PROCESSES

Aerobic composting is a managed process of adding the right amount of organic material that provides a carbon: nitrogen (C:N) ratio of about 30:1 and moisture content below 55% to 60%. This becomes complicated once you start adding high moisture food scraps to the mix. A solution to this dilemma is indoor fermentation using effective microorganisms (EM®).

EM is a patented product with specific organisms known to aid fermentation while also creating a critical mass of good organisms for rapid decomposition. The basic concept is to use the same bacteria, and yeast (fungi) used to make Kombucha, known to create healthy gut biomes - lactic acid bacteria and yeast. EM also uses phototrophic bacteria, which is commonly used in wastewater treatment.

Using a concentrated liquid of these three microorganisms, an inoculant is produced from wheat bran. In composting, carbon is the food; in fermentation, carbohydrates (sugars) are the food, and in putrefaction, protein is the energy source. So, with fermentation inoculant, EM is mixed with wheat bran (a carbon carrier), molasses (carbohydrate), and water. Wheat bran is the organism's home, molasses the food, and water the transport.

Kitchen scraps are kept dry, covered with the wheat bran inoculant, and isolated from the air (anaerobic). The fermented kitchen scraps are buried for two weeks and incorporated into the soil after that. The original organisms help other soil resident organisms flourish. They further break down the residue carbons in the batch using the available nitrogen.

INDUSTRIAL ANAEROBIC DIGESTION

Anaerobic digestion uses diverse populations of bacteria to break down organic waste. Primarily used in an industrial context, biological processes produce biogas with high-quality compost and cow-bedding byproducts.

In the industrial context, the primary sources of organic material include dairy manure, municipal wastewater, and waste from food processing factories, among others.

The controlled digestion of livestock manure, which captures the methane gas emissions, is an effective way of reducing greenhouse gases. Liquids from the digesting process contain fewer weed seeds and pathogens. These liquids can be used as a nutrient-rich agricultural fertilizer.

The Anaerobic Digestion Process

The first phase in anaerobic digestion happens when hydrolytic microorganisms produce extracellular enzymes that decompose complex organic polymers into soluble monomers. In the process, starch is broken into glucose, carbohydrates into sugars, proteins into amino acids, and lipids into long- and short-chain fatty acids. The enzymes produced by hydrolytic microorganisms include cellulase, amylase, protease, and lipase.

In the second phase in the anaerobic digestion process, the monomers are converted by fermentative bacteria to acetic, propionic, and butyric acids, as well as other minor products such as carbon dioxide, hydrogen, and acetic acid.

In the third phase, acetogenic bacteria convert the VTAs (volatile fatty acids) to acetate, CO2, and hydrogen.

The **last phase** is the anaerobic methane production process from the substrate created in phase three.

ANAEROBIC HOME COMPOSTING

Proteolytic microorganisms perform the decomposition process (putrefaction) in foods containing proteins. The process releases hydrogen sulfide, ammonia, and amino acids. Anaerobic processes are mainly performed by bacteria as most fungi are obligate aerobes. Nitrogen, phosphorus, and other nutrients are used by these organisms for protoplasm development and growth.

Humus, the final product of organic matter's anaerobic decomposition, may appear to decompose further when exposed to the air because of the reduction process. In terms of soil utilization, this oxidation is minor, takes place quickly, and has no effect. Anaerobic composting is referred to as a cold process. While there is some mesophilic activity, the mass never gets beyond 70 degrees Fahrenheit.

If contaminated materials are used for composting, the lack of heat is clearly a disadvantage. Pathogens and parasites can only be destroyed at high temperatures.

Because of the unfavorable environment, pathogenic organisms in anaerobic decomposition eventually die out.

The material must be held for six months to a year to ensure that pathogens, such as the eggs of Ascaris, are entirely destroyed. Ascaris is a nematode that is among the most resistant fecal-borne disease parasites in wastes. As a result, make compost this year and reap the benefits in the following year.

Anaerobic decomposition of organic material can, however, yield compost. Compostable materials, such as grass clippings, shredded leaves, kitchen waste, and small amounts of stable manure can all be decomposed using a heavy plastic bag.

4. COMPOSTING ELEMENTS

Scientists have only identified a fraction of the millions of microorganism species. For instance, there are an estimated 60,000 bacteria species, of which only 6% (3,600) have been named. Given that we've only had the technology to explore translucent cells for less than a century, I expect we'll see many new discoveries in the next decade.

The few microorganisms we've identified in this book, those involved in creating compost, have their own particular needs. We've learned that the organisms involved in aerobic composting have different needs than those engaged in anaerobic processes. We also briefly reviewed the microorganisms responsible for the fermentation process. In this chapter, we'll take a look at the needs of each group of microorganisms.

AEROBIC COMPOSTING ELEMENTS

As the heading indicates, the differentiating need of the organisms involved in the aerobic process is air (oxygen). Below are the other essential needs:

- A carbon to nitrogen ratio that can sustain microbial activity during the composting process. The carbon content must be sufficient to leave enough residual food to support continued biota activity once the compost is added to the soil.

- The management of temperature ranges. This is a balancing act between destroying pathogens and weed seeds in the mix without culling every member of the fungi family.

- The control of moisture content. To avoid anaerobic conditions, keep moisture levels below 60%.

- The distribution of active microorganisms throughout the process. This involves turning the pile and incorporating outer material into the inner high-activity arena.

- Managing available surface area for increased microbial activity, i.e., substrate particle size.

- The structure and composition of the compost pile – ensuring your microorganisms don't suffocate while still providing enough opportunity for heat and moisture distribution.

Please note that this chapter is purely focused on the needs of microorganisms. The actual detailed method to produce aerobic compost is reviewed in Chapter 6 – *Composting Production Methods*.

Composting progress is influenced by both physical and chemical factors. Varying temperatures at different stages of the process are critical in determining the success of composting. The moisture content and particle size of the ingredients affect the rate at which composting occurs. In addition, the size, shape, and content of the actual system affect the rate and type of aeration and the compost's tendency to retain or dissipate heat.

All these factors are influenced by the ratios of carbon and nitrogen in the materials (stock) being composted. Phosphorous and potassium also play a role, though their presence is generally assumed in the use of vegetation in the composting process. That said, an abundance of phosphorous can impede the rate with which arbuscular mycorrhizal (AM) fungi colonize plant roots. More on this in Chapter 6, under the heading *Inocula*. Trace elements haven't been found to impede the composting process rate. A pH of 6.5 to 8.0 is ideal (basically on the fringes of a neutral pH but leaning away from acidity).

Soil is ultimately a biological system. When it comes to soil health, the goal should be to create a habitat that is ideal for soil microorganisms. The following is a good starting point to creating a microorganism breeding colony.

HOW CARBON:NITROGEN (C:N) RATIOS AFFECT AEROBIC COMPOSTING

Unless you want to develop a best-in-class compost for specific uses, like inocula production for high-value plants, the general guidelines provided below are sufficient. You may find answers in the last chapter if you want more detail.

All fresh organic matter – like leaves, grass, yard debris, kitchen scraps, straw, hay, wood chips, sawdust, and paper – has a higher carbon content and lower nitrogen content. Fresher, greener materials have a higher nitrogen content, and older, drier materials have a lower nitrogen content. Theoretically, you want to start with a ratio of 30 parts of carbon to one of nitrogen (30:1).

Green materials (higher in nitrogen) include grass clippings, coffee grounds, and food waste. Brown materials (carbon leaders) are drier, more brittle, and include dry leaves, straw, wood chips, dry branches, and newspaper. Below is a list of common composting materials and their C:N ratios. While our goal is to get a C:N ratio of 30:1, we also have to manage the humidity levels in our mix. A good example, provided below, is the case study of composting with freshly mowed grass clippings and fall leaves.

Material	C:N Ratio
Vegetable wastes	10-20:1
Hairy vetch cover crop	11:1
Grass clippings	12-25:1
Poultry litter	13-18:1
Young alfalfa hay	13:1
Hay	15-30:1
Cow manure	17:1
Legume hay	17:1
Potatoes	18:1
Coffee grounds	20:1
Rotted barnyard manure	20:1
Horse manure	25:1
Mature alfalfa hay	25:1
Pea straw	29:1
Fall leaves	30-80:1
Corn silage	40:1
Straw	40-100:1
Corn stalks	60:1
Oat straw	70:1
Wheat straw	80:1
Rye straw	82:1
Bark	100-130:1
Wood chips and sawdust	100-500:1
Brush, wood chips	100-500:1
Shredded office paper	150-200:1
Newspaper	400-800:1
Cardboard	500:1

The Grass Clippings Composting Case Study

For ease of illustration, let's review a simple composting mix of high-nitrogen-content grass clippings with high-carbon-content fall leaves. Four factors are worth noting:

A. To avoid anaerobic conditions, the moisture content of the material in your compost pile should be less than 60%. On the other hand, microorganisms' activity ceases if your moisture content drops below 30%.

B. You are aiming for a carbon to nitrogen (C:N) ratio of between 30:1 to 33:1.

C. To avoid anaerobic conditions, you need air to flow. Grass clippings tend to mat. Because the grass blades are flat and wet (when freshly mowed), they stick to each other and prevent natural airflow. Leaves do the same thing, but this can be solved if we shred the leaves.

D. You want to increase your exposed surface area to maximize the available microorganisms' occupation.

Let's start with **Factor A** above – moisture. The moisture content of the completed compost mixture is an important consideration when determining the proper ratios of different materials to be used in composting. I go into more detail about how to do this in Chapter 6 – *Composting Production Methods.*

Basically, you take the weight of the freshly cut grass clippings and compare it to the dry weight of the same grass to determine the moisture percentage. I've done this a couple of times, and the average is 77%. It's no surprise then that it starts rotting if you leave a pile of grass clippings to stand for a day or two.

The solution to a dry mix is to add more green materials, and the reverse applies to wet mixes – add more dry matter. We've established that we must ensure moisture content below 60% to avoid anaerobic conditions. Our aim is to reduce the 77% moisture content in the clippings while retaining fresh clippings' nitrogen benefits – so drying it out isn't an option.

We need to add dry carbon matter that will absorb (or distribute) the excess 17% moisture. Even if we use dry leaves, their moisture content is still about 35%.

The following variables need to be known to balance the moisture between two ingredients of different moisture levels.

For the grass clippings:

- Q1   – the weight of lawn clippings   10 pounds

- G   – the moisture goal   60%

- M1   – the moisture content of the grass clippings   77%

For the shredded leaves:

- Q2   – the weight of shredded leaves   ?

- G   – the moisture goal   60%

- M2   – the moisture content of the shredded leaves   35%

Q2 = the absolute value of (10 pounds x 60) – (10 pounds x 77) / (35 – 60)

$$Q_2 = \frac{|\left(Q_1 \times G\right) - \left(Q_1 \times M_1\right)|}{M_2 - G}$$

= 170 / 25 = **6.8 pounds** of dry leaves mixed with the 10 pounds of grass clippings to get the mix equal to or below the 60% moisture threshold to prevent anaerobic conditions.

Therefore, for every 10 pounds of grass clippings, we need to add about seven pounds of leaves. For now, we're only considering moisture levels, and next, we'll consider the effect on the carbon:nitrogen ratio. For now, we have a mix of ten pounds of grass clippings and seven pounds of dry shredded leaves.

To satisfy **Factor B**, let us, for the moment, ignore the moisture in the grass clippings. To capitalize on the high nitrogen levels in grass clipping, we need to mix the clipping into a shredded leaf mass. Dry leaves have a nitrogen level of 0.75%, and carbon content is 50% carbon (the rest is cellulose and tough lignin). The C:N ratio of our batch of dry leaves is 66:1. I calculated the ratio by dividing the 50 by 0.75. What would the standard shredded leaves to grass clippings be to obtain a C:N ratio of 30:0?

Let's work it out. The average glass clippings' C:N ratio is 17.5:1, with a nitrogen content of between 2.4% and 3.4%. Let's assume we have an average batch of 2.8% nitrogen and 49% carbon. We want to solve the amount of leaves to add to the 10 pounds of grass clippings to get a C:N ratio of 30:1.

The variables we will need are:

Regarding the lawn clippings

- Q1   – the weight of lawn clippings   10 pounds

- N1   – the percentage of nitrogen in the grass clippings   2.8%

- R   – the desired end carbon ratio   30

- C1   – the carbon percentage of the grass clippings   49%

- M1   – the moisture content of the grass clippings   77%

We will need the same information for the leaves, except the weight of the leaves, as that is what we want to determine.

- Q2   – the quantity of leaves needed for the mix   ?

- N2   – the leaves' nitrogen percentage   0.75%

- C2   – the leaves' carbon percentage   50%

- M2   – the moisture content of the leaves   35%

$$Q_2 = \frac{Q_1 \times N_1 \times \left(R - \frac{C_1}{N_1}\right) \times (100 - M_1)}{N_2 \times \left(\frac{C_2}{N_2} - R\right) \times (100 - M_2)}$$

$$Q_2 = \frac{10 \times 2.8 \times \left(30 - \frac{49}{2.8}\right) \times (100 - 77)}{0.75 \times \left(\frac{50}{0.75} - 30\right) \times (100 - 35)}$$

$$Q_2 = \frac{28 \times (30 - 17.5) \times 23}{0.75 \times (66.66 - 30) \times 65}$$

We need 8050 / 1787 = **4.5 pounds** of shredded leaves per 10 pounds of grass clippings to get our desired carbon to nitrogen mix of 30:1.

So, to get to a 30:1 ratio, for every 10 pounds of grass clippings, you only need about 4.6 pounds of dry leaves. But as we established, we need 6.8 pounds of leaves to manage moisture levels. What is a gardener to do? What do you choose when there's a choice between accepting lower C:N ratios or high moisture content?

If we opt for the safer dryer conditions and add the leaves required to get the moisture level below 60%, what will our C:N ratio be? We need to get the representative fraction of each part to the whole, multiply that with the original ratios and add the two together to get the C:N ratio of the resulting mix.

Grass clippings

- W1　　　　 – weight of grass clippings　　　　　　　　　10 pounds

- R1　　　　　 – C:N ratio of grass clippings　　　　　　　　17.5

Shredded Leaves

- W2　　　　　– weight of shredded leaves　　　　　　　　　　6.8 pounds

- R2　　　　　- C:N ratio of shredded leaves　　　　　　　　　　66.66

A = the C:N ratio of the mixture.

$$A = \left(W_1 \div \left(W_1 + W_2 \right) \right) \times R_1 + \left(W_2 \div \left(W_1 + W_2 \right) \right) \times R_2$$

$$A = \left(0.595 \times 17.5 \right) + \left(0.405 \times 66.66 \right) = 37.4$$

A = 37.4, thus the new ratio of the mix can be stated as approximately 37:1.

We aimed for 30 parts of carbon matter for every part of nitrogen. We have an excess of carbon in our mix that may slow the process down. But, remember that the carbon is continually being reduced in the composting process – some as carbon dioxide respiration and some for microorganisms' cellular development. The final compost mix ratio ought to be about 10:1 once it is stabilized.

So, while the 37:1 ratio will delay the speed of our initial composting process, as the microorganisms consume the carbon, releasing carbon dioxide, the ratio of nitrogen will increase. So, it won't be long before we get to the optimum threshold 33:1 ratio when things speed up.

If, however, we opt to add fewer leaves, focussing on starting with the optimal 30 to 33:1 ratio, our moisture will be more than the crucial 60%. It won't be long before there's the distinct rot as anaerobic conditions set in. To salvage the batch, you will need to add wood shavings – more dry-matter carbon. It's better to start with a mixture with a total humidity factor of less than 60%.

Another exciting consideration, in this case, is bioavailability. Bioavailability is a term that describes the levels of readily accessible nitrogen and carbon in a composting mix. Grass clippings are an excellent example of high bioavailability. If you left your clippings on the lawn, it would reduce the need to add nitrogen by as much as 50% – halving the amount of nitrogen you need to add. That is because the nitrogen in the grass is readily available to the lawn below. This characteristic of grass clippings makes it ideal as a nitrogen-adding composting component.

On the other hand, leaves have limited use in traditional composting – limited but still valuable. Because the carbon in leaves is encased in cellulose and lignin, its bioavailability is limited. Usually, it's fungi that break leaves down into mold. In traditional hot composting, the combination of a diverse population of microorganisms does the job. The point is that even though theoretically our leaf/clippings mix is now at 37:1, the reality is that a lot of that carbon is not bioavailable. This helps solve the challenge of a high carbon ratio – the carbon referred won't be part of the process until the shredders and fungi have made a meal of the lignin.

Carbon

Carbon is the primary food source for aerobic decomposition microorganisms. Some of the available carbon provides energy, and some is combined with nitrogen for cellular growth (body maintenance). The average microorganism's cell mass is approximately 88% carbon, and humans, in comparison, are 23% carbon. Microorganisms have an average C:N ratio is 8:1, something they need to maintain to stay alive – even in the soil.

While you may start your composting pile with the standard 30 parts of carbon to every nitrogen part (30:1), ending with a mere 10:1 ratio is typical (and ideal). In the composting process, some carbon dioxide is released during respiration. As a result, the carbon content of a compost pile is continuously decreasing (and the nitrogen percentage is therefore increasing). Not all weight reduction is due to carbon loss, though, and some of the loss is in the form of water vapor. In the consumption of carbon, microorganisms produce heat, CO_2, water, and (thankfully) humus.

The starting ratio of 30 to 33:1 carbon to nitrogen is essential because:

- The lowest level of carbon suggested is 24:1. At that ratio, the microorganisms will consume all the carbon – 16 units for energy and 8 units to maintain their own cell structure. That will mean that the carbon available is too low to sustain the lives of microorganisms in the soil.

- If your carbon content is too high, the process will be slow to start and take a long time. Suppose you add too much carbon to the soil without an established soil biota. In that case, the continued high activity of the microorganisms in the ground will tie up soil nutrients (immobilization), making them inaccessible to plants. Only once the soil biota is stabilized (when some organisms perish and release the nitrogen in ionic form) will plants benefit.

- Adding compost with a 10:1 ratio will result in a temporary nitrogen surplus (mineralization). This is why we always try to achieve a C:N ratio of about 30:1. That way, the resident microbes can readily decompose the compost pile while leaving some shelter and food for microbes after the compost is applied to the soil.

Nitrogen

Nitrogen is the most abundant gas on earth and represents 78% of the atmosphere. Every breath you take is mainly nitrogen. Sixteen percent of protein content is nitrogen in the form of amino acids. You may have heard me referring to adding a urine solution to leaf composting. Well, the average human's urine is 11% to 18% nitrogen.

Cellular material, amino acids, and proteins are all made from nitrogen, which is continuously recycled by microorganisms. Nitrogen incorporated into microorganisms' cells is released when the organism dies. The C:N ratio decreases over the composting period because a large portion of the carbon is continuously released while most nitrogen is recycled.

One of the most prolific nitrogen producers is the arbuscular mycorrhiza (AM). Most soils contain these naturally occurring fungi. They establish a mutualistic symbiotic relationship with most crop plants by colonizing the roots. Crops such as rapeseed, broccoli, spinach, and sugar beet are notable for not forming this symbiosis. In addition to helping plants absorb soil minerals and strengthen their resistance to disease and drought, AM fungi also improve plant health. Mineral nutrients like phosphorus, zinc, and copper, which are not readily available in soil water solutions, are better absorbed by plants. Without mycorrhizal fungi, these nutrients can be absorbed just a few millimeters away from the plant's roots. These immobile nutrients can be extracted from 8 cm or more away from the roots of AM fungi thanks to their thread-like hyphae strands. We will review how to boost their availability when reviewing the inoculum later.

An initial C:N ratio of 24:1 to 40:1 is recommended for rapid composting. The composting process is slowed if the C:N ratio is above the optimal range because of excess carbon. A lack of nitrogen is the primary constraint in this case. Microorganisms have a hard time utilizing the excess carbon because they have a limited nitrogen supply.

The C:N ratio must be reduced to a more appropriate level through several life cycles of organisms. Your end product will be carbon deficient if you have too much nitrogen (and limited carbon) in your raw material. Ammonia (NH3) or ammonium (NH4+), both unstable forms of nitrogen, will form if the process of protein decomposition is interrupted due to a lack of carbon. Toxic concentrations of gaseous ammonia or leaching nitrogen from the pile could contaminate nearby groundwater or surface waters.

However, the C:N ratio does not always accurately reflect the amount of nutrients available to microorganisms in compost. As mentioned earlier, bioavailability needs to be considered as well as balancing the C:N ratio. Woody material bound by decay-resistant lignins is more difficult to decompose, whereas material containing simple sugars, like fruit waste, decomposes quickly. Keratin is the only nitrogen source that is resistant to decay. Keratin is the fibrous protein tissue used in DNA testing – hair and nails. It is also found in horns, feathers, and wool in the animal kingdom.

WATER

As with all living creatures on earth, microorganisms require water to live. Additionally, the mobility of these tiny creatures depends on a fluid-filled environment – for them and for nutrients. Water is also the platform for chemical reactions.

Of course, too much of a good thing can be detrimental. As we saw with the grass clippings case study, we do not want the pile to become too wet and cut off the air supply to the microorganisms. If this happens, we'll have an odiferous anaerobic system. For composting, the ideal moisture content must therefore be a compromise between ensuring adequate moisture for microorganisms to function and ensuring adequate oxygen flow to maintain aerobic conditions.

The recommended moisture content for composting is between 40% and 65%. When the moisture content drops below 15%, all microorganisms hibernate. Evaporation and precipitation contribute to changes in the compost pile's moisture content during the composting process. Enough water and porosity must be maintained at all times during the process.

Moisture content decreases during the composting process, and additional water may be needed depending on the climate. Moisture content considerations are also influenced by the material used in the compost mix. For example, moisture content can be higher in porous materials than densely packed ones.

Additionally, moisture serves as a cooling mechanism. The compost pile's air and compost material are heated by the composting process, evaporating water in the process. Compost piles may overheat if the compost pile becomes too dry during the thermophilic stage.

OXYGEN

Aerobic microorganisms cannot survive without oxygen. Anaerobic microbes take over the compost pile if adequate oxygen is not provided, slowing down the composting process. This state of affairs is most easily recognized by the foul odors released. It can be remedied by adding some dry materials like wood shavings. To maintain aerobic conditions, an oxygen concentration of 6% is required. We'll review aeration techniques in Chapter 6. Whatever method you use to aerate your pile, keep in mind that your microorganisms live in a thin water layer. Balancing moisture and airflow is essential. Getting this right is covered in the section below – Composting Pile Characteristics.

HEAT

During the active composting period, the compost pile experiences a wide range of temperatures. Some microorganisms cannot survive when the temperature changes, while others thrive in new conditions. There are three temperature ranges in a home composting system during the active composting period. These temperature ranges are psychrophilic, mesophilic, and thermophilic, based on the types of prominent microorganisms in a pile at those temperatures.

Temperatures lower than 50 degrees Fahrenheit are considered psychrophilic. Psychrophilic organisms are most prevalent at the initiation of the process and during curing. The mesophilic organisms are active at temperatures between 50 and 105 degrees Fahrenheit, while thermophilic microorganisms are responsible for temperatures above that.

However, the defined temperature ranges do not exclude the possibility of the broader presence of other microorganisms. These *other* organisms are known as facultative organisms for their ability to live under more than one specific environmental condition. Temperature ranges provide a rough distinction between the temperatures at which different microorganisms reach their maximum growth rates and efficiencies.

When composting begins, there is usually a short lag before the temperature rises rapidly. This lag time is required for the microbial population to grow. Microorganisms don't reproduce but exponentially multiply – each cell subdividing through binary fission. One becomes two, and two become four. This only happens if enough energy and food materials (carbon and nitrogen) are available. The multiplication cycles are between 6 minutes and 24 hours. Generally, your microorganism population doubles every 12 hours.

The self-insulating compost traps heat generated by microbial activity as the population breaks down the most readily degradable material and grows. As the microbial population grows and diversifies, the temperature increases steadily through the psychrophilic and mesophilic temperature ranges. Depending on the operation, compost piles can take anywhere from two to three days to transition from mesophilic to thermophilic composting.

Because of the diversity of the microbial population, a wide range of materials, from simple, easily degradable ones to more complex, decay-resistant ones like cellulose, can be decomposed. Expect a rise in temperatures, with a maximum of 130 to 160 degrees Fahrenheit (55 to 70 degrees Celsius). Some microorganisms create a hard shell (called spores) to protect themselves. The microbial activity begins to decline as soon as the readily degradable material and oxygen run out or if the temperature rises too high and becomes harmful to their function.

When the substrate becomes depleted, more heat is lost from the pile than is generated as microbial activity decreases and the pile cools. Various microorganisms repopulate the pile as the temperature drops below thermophilic levels. At the same time, spores germinate as conditions improve and migrate from cooler spots. It's these microorganisms that keep the decomposition process moving along.

Depending on the process, the compost pile can stay in the thermophilic range for anywhere from 10 to 60 days. Aerate the pile to reactivate active composting once the temperature drops below 105 degrees Fahrenheit. Active composting is never determined to be finished at a specific point. When the pile conditions are such that microbial activity cannot increase enough to reheat the pile, it is usually considered complete and ready for curing.

As microbial activity decreases during the curing process, the composted materials become more stable. When organic acids and decay-resistant compounds continue to decompose, they are stabilized by other processes like the formation of humic compounds and generating nitrate-nitrogen. Curing has the benefit of introducing beneficial fungi to the pile, which helps the compost's disease-fighting properties.

Microbiological activity has decreased and is now operating at a lower level, resulting in the pile generating less heat and decreasing temperature. Proper moisture and oxygen management are still required during the curing period to maintain microbial activity.

COMPOST PILE CHARACTERISTICS

When developing a compost mix, the physical characteristics of the ingredients must be taken into account as well. Aeration, decomposition, and a pile's ability to maintain aerobic conditions are all influenced by various physical characteristics. In terms of compost mix, physical characteristics, porosity, texture, and structure are all critical.

Compost Pile Porosity

The amount of air space in a compost mixture is known as porosity, and this has an impact on the amount of resistance a pile has to airflow. Airflow is restricted when the pores in a material become clogged with water due to high moisture content.

As the amount of oxygen available to microorganisms decreases, anaerobic activity takes over. A more uniform mixture of materials improves porosity by ensuring that air spaces are not interrupted. Larger particles aid airflow, but their reduced surface area makes them undesirable. Decomposition increases with compost surface area because most microbial activity occurs on the particles' surfaces within a thin liquid layer.

Texture

The surface area available to microorganisms is texture, which refers to the relative proportion of different particle sizes in a material. The more abundant the surface area exposed to microbial activity, the more effective the composting process. By using methods like selection and grinding to reduce particle size, you're also increasing the amount of material exposed to microbial decomposition on the pile's surface.

Structure

Structure refers to a particle's ability to withstand compacting and settling during transportation. It's essential for composting because it helps keep the material porous. When the decomposing material settles and closes off air spaces in a pile, the composting process slows.

Less porous material (like grass clippings) lose their structure more quickly than highly absorbent material. Even if a composting mixture contains all the necessary ingredients, it may not support rapid composting without the proper structure. Compost particle size must balance porosity, surface area, and structural enhancement.

THE POTENTIAL OF HYDROGEN (PH)

The pH of your materials does not impact the composting process significantly. Because different microorganisms thrive at different pH levels, the pH will determine which organisms are most active. Between 6.5 and 8.0 is the ideal microbial activity range. Despite this, the process of composting continues at higher and lower pH levels, such as 5.0 and 9.0. Composting generally stabilizes pH between 7.5 and 8.0 at the end of the process, irrespective of initial pH. Compost has the same effect on the soil it is added to – stabilizing the pH.

The original compost mix and the subsequent production of various intermediates during the composting process affect the pH levels. It is common for the pH to fall to between 4.0 and 5.0 during the first few days of active composting. An abundance of a carbonaceous substrate can increase organic acid intermediates, lowering the pH in anaerobic zones. Aerobic microorganisms, mainly bacteria, do not do well in acidic environments, and their absence may slow the composting process down. Because there are organisms that can use the acidic compounds as a substrate for composting, the process will continue, though slower.

The pH rises as these organisms break down the acidic compounds. This means that pH adjustments are unnecessary in most cases because of the compost's natural buffering capacity. When nitrogen-rich material is to be composted, the pH is a concern. Nitrogenous compounds can be converted to ammonia at a pH above 8.5. In addition to slowing down the composting process, this ammonia formation promotes nitrogen loss through ammonia volatilization. The pH may have to be lowered below 8.0 in these cases.

Acidic conditions in the early stages of composting may necessitate raising the pH, but this is rare. Because an appropriate microbial population takes longer to form in acidic conditions, increasing the pH accelerates the composting process. Organic acid intermediates, which are responsible for most of the odorous compounds generated at a composting site, can be prevented by keeping the pH of the composting site at a basic level. Lime ($Ca(OH)_2$) is the most common additive used for this purpose. When adjusting the pH with an additive, ammonia volatilization and nitrogen losses increase because the pH remains alkaline longer, so beware.

ANAEROBIC COMPOSTING ELEMENTS

Every opportunity to compost must be used. While I'm not a great fan of anaerobic composting, trench composting and Bokashi have both given me great results. According to the United States Environmental Protection Agency (EPA)[3], Americans recovered over 69 million tons of municipal solid waste (MSW) through recycling and almost 25 million tons through composting. This is 1.16 pounds per person per day for recycling and 0.42 pounds per person per day for composting. Food composting curbside collection programs served 6.1 million households in 2017, the most recent year for which information is available.

---

3   *https://www.epa.gov/sustainable-management-food/reducing-impact-wasted-food-feeding-soil-and-composting*

Nature, using microorganisms, can effectively recycle its elements—including carbon, hydrogen, oxygen, nitrogen, and other minerals for new growth. She uses two biological processes to convert organic matter into more simplistic (plant-available) forms.

- Suppose there's a supply of air containing at least 6% oxygen. In that case, the organic matter is degraded by oxidation, dissipating carbon dioxide, heat, and water vapor, and producing humus. We refer to these oxidation reactions as **aerobic composting**.

- When no oxygen is available, organic matter is degraded by reduction, and CH4 and CO2 are perspired. Reduction reactions occur under what is referred to as **anaerobic** conditions.

Anaerobic degradation occurs in the absence of oxygen and through a series of biological processes. Three microorganism groups are responsible for the three stages in anaerobic digestion:

- **Hydrolysis.** The first group of microorganisms secretes enzymes that hydrolyze polymeric materials to monomers. Complex carbohydrates are reduced into simpler compounds, and anaerobic bacteria transform organic matter into less complex soluble compounds. The bacteria break down proteins and carbohydrates into amino acids and simple sugars and reduce lipids to fatty acids.

- **Acidogenesis.** In a combination of fermentation and anaerobic oxidation reactions, acidogenic bacteria convert amino acids, simple sugars, and lipids to acetic acid, CO2, and H2. Fermentation and acidogenesis co-occur, but different microbial populations are involved.

- **Methanogenesis.** Methanogenic archaea convert acetic acid, carbon dioxide, and hydrogen into methane and carbon dioxide, a combination of biogas.

In a nutshell, this is what happens in an anaerobic process like trench composting:

- Acidogenic and methanogenic microbial populations must be balanced for anaerobic treatment or reduction of organic wastes.

- Proteins in organic residues bind a large portion of the nitrogen, making it unavailable to plants unless they are biologically converted. When ammonium

(NH4) is dissolved in water, organic-bound nitrogen is reduced to ammonium (NH4). Ammonia is released as a byproduct of bacteria's breakdown of organic materials during digestion. Methanogen growth can be inhibited and biogas production reduced by high ammonia concentrations. Ammonium and inorganic phosphorus compounds may build up in livestock and poultry manure because of their high nitrogen and phosphorus content.

- In anaerobic digestion of sulfur-containing organic waste, sulfur is reduced to hydrogen sulfide (H2S), which smells like rotten eggs and is commonly found in anaerobic waste processing.

- As the temperature rises, anaerobic decomposition becomes more efficient and more rapid.

5. SELECTING WHERE TO COMPOST

Residential composting operations require some location consideration. Depending on the scale of your composting efforts, you should be cognizant of local and state requirements. Some local counties require permits for more extensive operations. These are generally concerned about managing pollution, odor, runoff, and other environmental risks. It may be prudent to check in with your local government to establish if any regulations apply. For more significant scaled operations, checking in with USDA Soil Conservation Services (SCS) is advised.

This chapter will review some of the considerations of *residential* composting – from kitchen composting to small-scale composting operations for community gardens. This book is not intended for scaled operations that require heavier machinery, impervious all-weather roads, and extensive management. More significant operations are required to manage air quality, water pollution, fire, and other potential hazards. Issues of health and safety, noise management, leachate management, and methane gas management all fall outside of the scope of this book, which is meant for residential composting using mainly local supplies of organic matter.

COMPOSTING AT HOME

I encourage composting at any scale. Even on a small scale, composting can add significant value to your garden – indoors or outdoors. The cost of composting your kitchen waste is negligible. The average American household produces about 700 pounds of compostable kitchen scraps per year. That is a lot of fertility potential right there.

I prefer the fermentation process that uses the Bokashi effective microorganisms (EM®). We'll cover Bokashi composting in the next chapter, but let's focus on getting readers comfortable with the idea of having a composting facility indoors. Fermentation processes are odorless, hygienic, and can add value to potting soils for indoor gardeners. For those who plan to use their fermented food scraps as part of the trench composting process, pre-fermentation reduces the decomposition time from one year to a month.

INDOOR COMPOSTING SITE

Gathering your kitchen waste for composting can take on many formats. One way is to take the scraps directly to the compost pile outdoors, add it, and cover it with some sawdust to balance C:N ratios, keep flies at bay and balance moisture. Another way is to add your kitchen scraps to a container that seals, limits aeration and stands on your kitchen countertop. This section looks at the latter option.

These containers, or bins, have false, perforated bottoms that allow fluids to drain off. The bottom section has a little tap that allows you to drain the accumulated liquid. This is how the Bokashi bin works, but the addition of EM inoculated wheat bran keeps the organic material dryer and promotes fermentation.

Indoor *fermentation* is generally done in a bin that resembles the one described above – a bin that facilitates fermentation, allows fluids to drain away from the scraps, excludes flies, and limits airflow. After making the last addition of fresh scraps to your bin and covering them with a thin layer of Bokashi bran, seal the container and store for a further two weeks. After that, the fermented scraps will be ready for composting – either in a trench, on your compost pile, or indoors in a sealable bucket.

A Bokashi bin can be as big as you want it to be. Bin sizes vary from two to five gallons. The determining factor of the size you choose is the time it will take you to fill the bin. Ideally, you want a bin that you can fill within two to four weeks. It takes two weeks for the full bin to ferment, so a bin that takes about two weeks to fill allows you to rotate between two bins (one being filled and one fermenting). The risks of something going wrong with a batch increases the longer you take to fill the bin.

The best place for your in-process compost bin is near your work area in the kitchen – either on the countertop or under the counter. Fermentation bins are exceptionally hygienic, so keeping them on the fridge is also an option. If you prefer, you can keep it in the broom closet or pantry. The location of your indoor composting site should allow easy access.

For the second phase of indoor Bokashi processing, after storing your sealed full bin for two weeks, add garden soil, mix well and store for a further month. This is typically done in a dedicated sealable container (different from the Bokashi bin). Ideally, you want to store this out of direct sunlight. Keep the vessel in storage for three weeks or more in a convenient place. After about 21 days, the product in the container can be used as potting soil – it'll be ultra-fertile potting soil.

BACKYARD COMPOSTING SITES

Outdoors, your location should be easy to access and have adequate drainage. A wire, mesh, or porous base can be used as a foundation before turning the soil under the compost bin for best results. A pallet is a good choice. Using the pegs provided, fasten the bin to the ground. When you're not adding or maintaining the pile, make sure the lid is closed and the lock is engaged.

The best location for a compost pile or bin is at least 20 feet away from your house and 12 feet from other structures, such as sheds. Place it in an area that gets partial sun near a garden hose that will allow you to moisten the layers. The pile will work best in a location where drying winds will have little effect, i.e., in a protected area.

A flat, open space that is not at risk of flooding or runoff to surface waters and wells is best for the location. Ideally, I prefer to allow sufficient adjacent space to turn the compost – either a bin or a structured pile. Keep the areas in front and above the pile or bin clear so that you can work without any problems.

A bin is not essential. Some people use bins to keep the pile tidy, to help retain heat and moisture, or because they live in a neighborhood where a bin would be more appropriate than an open pile. Concrete blocks, wooden pallets, wire mesh, 45-gallon drums, or garbage cans are options people use to build their own compost bins.

My preferred option is to make a wooden bin with three compartments. Enclosed, spherical, and tumbler composting bins are just some of the other options available. Another essential consideration for backyard composters is positioning your composting operations to avoid interfering with yard activities.

The process of building a composting system tailored to your needs will be outlined for you in Chapter 7. Each method has its benefits and disadvantages, so your compost site selection will be influenced by the process that best serves your needs.

Particular attention should be given to your relations with your neighbor regarding your composting operations. It could save you much frustration if you don't need to navigate a complaint from the neighbor after the process is underway. Depending on the methods you use (covered in the next chapter), you can help neighbors understand the benefits of composting. Composting done appropriately does not attract rodents, flies, or other pests and scavengers.

COMMUNITY GARDEN COMPOSTING SITES

As a result of permit exemptions, small-scale compost operations, such as community gardens, are allowed to go ahead with their operations without the need for unnecessary permits. Many states have incorporated permit exemptions for on-farm and small-scale composters because of the lower risk or hazard. On-site composting can also be made easier by modifying local zoning regulations.

Larger scale, non-commercial composting operations require special attention. While some states and counties do not regulate community composting facilities, it is highly advisable to check legislation in your county. Some states even have grants available to fund community composting initiatives, so getting more information could help your operations significantly.

Below we review some factors that may influence the location of a small-scale community composting facility. Collaborating with businesses, households, and restaurants could be a benefit.

A well-drained area is ideal for composting, but it should be kept free of runoff or leachate so as not to pollute local waterways. If you expect some runoff, a containment pond will be beneficial. Your soil type needs to be considered, too, as any soil courser than sandy loam is unsuitable. Also, note where local flood lines are on the property. Ideal locations include slopes of between 2% and 4%, concrete or packed soil or gravel, and sites that drain into a containment pond.

Windrows should be laid out parallel to the slope. This keeps the windrow from obstructing the pad's drainage and gives easy access. Pad problems can occur on slopes greater than 6% because they are more likely to be prone to erosion.

Composting near the barn or where organic matter is collected is usually the most convenient location on the site. However, the ease of a particular location must be weighed against factors such as the area, proximity to neighbors, visibility, drainage, and runoff control. To get the most out of a composting location, you might have to make a few adjustments, such as grading or drainage.

Sites near sensitive areas, like schools, hospitals, and nursing homes, should be avoided. In addition, the composting site should be far enough away from the homes of nearby residents so that they won't be disturbed by it. Your PR effort will be less effective once a complaint has been lodged, so maintain transparency with your neighbors and key stakeholders from the onset of planning the facility.

Community composting excludes sanitary wastewater treatment facility residual but includes the following source-separated materials: vegetative material; food material; agricultural material; biodegradable products; biodegradable paper; clean wood; or yard waste. Tracking the quantities used is important.

LEGISLATIVE GUIDELINES FOR COMMUNITY COMPOSTING

- Composting operations should be located on the premises of a community garden.

- The composting operation is a tangent activity of the primary activity of maintaining a community garden.

- The composting operation prevents the discharge of pollutants to air, water, or other natural resources.

- The facilities of the composting operation are adequate to handle the projected volume of material to be processed.

- The location of the composting operation area is on loam soil – not excessively drained sand or impermeable clay.

- Composting facility plans need to be submitted to local authorities for approval:

- Describing the intended composting method.

- Including composting site location information.

- A site plan must show the layout of the composting operations, including areas for unloading, mixing, windrows, and curing.

- A description of the feedstock to be used and the compost recipe.

- The source(s) of the compostable materials.

- The collection/delivery rota of the materials if these are sourced offsite. Offsite materials present risks for pathogens and other contaminants in the mix.

- Compost end-use information, including estimated volume and percentage of the total quantity of compost produced for a calendar year to be used on the community garden.

- An odor management plan – dominant wind directions in relation to residential, school, or other public areas must inform the location of the site of the composting operations.

- The community composting facility may not occupy more than 10% of the total community garden's land area.

- At least 25% of the composted material must be from the community garden.

- The community garden must be the primary user of the compost produced.

- The community garden composting facility will actively prevent the illegal dumping of waste materials.

- The composting facility will adhere to USDA composting guidelines.

- The composting operations will have documented plans to minimize odors, noise, the drift of materials, vectors, and risk to humans or the environment – and implement the plans.

- The composting operations will maintain and keep accurate records of all the essential elements of the composting operations.

- Some states require that you maintain stocks of organic materials to ensure a carbon to nitrogen ratio of 30:1. This includes sufficient carbon-rich material to mix with fresh green material as these become available.

- All materials received for composting shall be source-separated and recorded as such.

- Vegetables, food materials, grass clippings, green plant material, fish waste, and fats will be incorporated into high-carbon material sufficiently to mask their presence.

- The community garden will not become a primary storage area for composted material.

- All composting operations and facilities will be located at least 250 feet from a private well, 300 feet from a residence, and 100 feet from a property line.

- The composting operations will prevent the unpermitted discharge of pollutants to air, water, or other natural resources.

The synopsis above is merely a guideline. Local laws and bylaws should be consulted as the first step of the planning phase of a composting operation in a community garden. Some community gardens are occupied by individual tenants with allotments. A cooperative process of making compost could have the benefits of scale, making the process faster and concentrating effort.

6. AEROBIC COMPOSTING

Choices of composting methods are generally influenced by the material being composted, the preferred level of control, any time constraints, and the volume of organic waste to be processed. Another essential factor is the desired end product. In this chapter, we'll explore aerobic compost production methods.

Also referred to as traditional composting, aerobic compost manufacturing can take numerous forms. What differentiates aerobic composting from other processes is the essential role of oxygen. The availability of oxygen to microorganisms within the composting process influences materials included, material particle size, and moisture levels. In conjunction with moisture and temperatures, oxygen is also an essential indicator in the production management process.

In industrial applications, aerobic processes decompose sanitary wastewater treatment facilities' residues (biosolids). Such processes are not within the scope of this book. This book focuses on assisting the gardener in becoming a master of their craft, for which aerobic composting is an essential skill.

Within this section, we'll explore hot composting, a **managed process** of using organic materials to produce humus inhabited by an array of microorganisms. We'll also review the aerated static pile process and the aerobic in-vessel composting process.

HOT COMPOSTING

In contrast to static pile composting, hot composting is a managed process. It requires the composter to plan, organize, monitor, and respond to fluctuating conditions to create stabilized humus with a high population of diverse microorganisms. The product should also be free of pathogens and weed seeds.

During hot aerobic composting, microorganisms feed on the carbon (C) and nitrogen (N) of organic material and consume oxygen (O), generating considerable heat and releasing CO_2 and water vapor (H_2O). As much as 50% of the original organic matter weight is lost in the composting process. Composting reduces the weight and volume of the composted material, producing one of the most effective soil-health improvement materials.

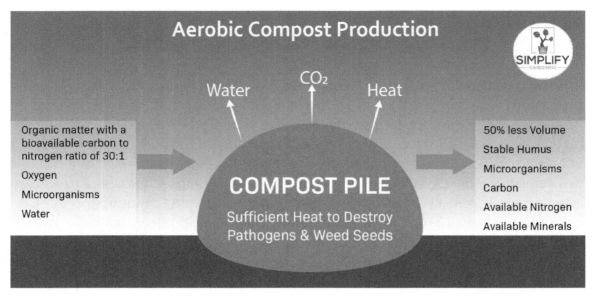

Figure 61: Aerobic Composting Dynamics

Hot composting is the fastest composting process. However, process speed and finished humus quality depend on various conditions. The ideal conditions include:

- An optimal environment of bioavailable carbon to nitrogen ratio of 30:1 for the proliferation of microorganisms throughout the process.

- Continuous availability of oxygen throughout the pile and the process.

- Sufficient moisture to permit microbial activity without hindering the availability of localized oxygen (aeration).

- Managed temperatures, a critical indicator of vigorous microbial activity in optimal conditions.

- A composition of carbon- and nitrogen-rich substrates that provide microorganisms sufficiently available surface areas upon which to act, while preventing compaction and anaerobic conditions.

WHAT CAN'T BE COMPOSTED

✗ Boxes that contained frozen food
✗ Plastic-coated cardboard containers (often used for liquid products, like milk)
✗ Earbuds
✗ Pet feces
✗ Carnivore feces (including dogs and cats)
✗ Glossy paper
✗ Flowers sold commercially – they're treated with antibacterial substances
✗ Styrofoam
✗ Chipboard
✗ Walnut shells and Black Walnut leaves—they can be toxic to plants
✗ Persistent herbicides
✗ Equine or bovine manure from farms that treat their feed crops with Aminopyralid
✗ Lawn clippings if you use a broadleaf herbicide that contains Clopyralid
✗ Herbicides from the Bipyridyliums family also have low microbial decomposition rates. Gramoxone and Diquat are examples.

WHAT COMPOSTS WELL

✓ Plant material, such as:
  o Grass clippings
  o Leaves (shredded)
  o Weeds
  o Flowers
  o Shrub trimmings
  o Tree trimmings (mill thicker branches)
  o Potted plants
  o Yard debris

✓ Kitchen scraps
  o Vegetable scraps
  o Expired fruit
  o Eggshells
  o Coffee grounds
  o Tea leaves (not the teabag)
  o Peels (including citrus)
  o Spoiled food

- o Wine corks
- o Toothpicks
- o Freezer-burned vegetables and fruits
- o Dregs from juice, beer, wine
- o Nutshells (excluding walnut)
- o Bread, tortillas, pitas
- o Cereal and crackers
- o Chips (tortilla, potato, etc.)
- o Cooked pasta, rice, other grains
- o Almond, soy, rice, and coconut milk

✓ Household waste
- o Hair and fur
- o Dryer lint
- o Vacuum contents & floor sweepings
- o Pencil shavings
- o Loofahs (the organic type)
- o Cotton, wool, linen, silk, hemp, burlap, felt
- o Used matches
- o Indoor plant trimmings
- o Nail clippings
- o Aquarium water, algae, plants
- o Spent potting soil
- o Dead blossoms
- o Bamboo skewers
- o Potpourri
- o Beer and wine-making leftovers
- o Evergreen garlands and wreaths
- o Jack-o-lanterns
- o Dry dog, cat, fish food
- o Crepe paper streamers
- o Yarn, thread, string, rope, twine
- o Cork board

✓ Paper products
- o Shredded paper
- o Food-soiled paper or cardboard
- o Cardboard

- o Plant starch compostable containers, dishware and utensils
- o Paper bags
- o Paper towel and toilet paper cores
- o Tissues, paper napkins, and paper towels
- o Wrapping and tissue paper (no ribbons, foil, or tape)
- o Uncoated paper cups & plates
- o Compostable bags made from plant starches
- o Paper baking cups
- o Paper table cloths
- o Cereal boxes
- o Paper egg cartons
- o Pizza boxes

✓ Wood product (from untreated wood)
- o Wood shavings
- o Sawdust
- o Shredded wood
- o Bark

✓ Manures (herbivores)
- o Bovine (Cattle) – see exclusion list above
- o Equine (Horse) – see exclusion list above
- o Rabbits
- o Chicken
- o Goat
- o Sheep
- o Alpaca
- o Game (Hare and Elephant – and all the herbivores in between)
- o Turkey litter
- o Swine manure

✓ Acquired farm products
- o Hay
- o Teff
- o Straw
- o Lucerne
- o Corn Silage

AEROBIC COMPOSTING PROCESS

Composting begins as soon as conditions are suitable for microorganism activity – oxygen, carbon food, nitrogen fuel, and a film of water over the carbon matter. Microorganisms are present everywhere – in your mouth, gut, and on almost every surface. Whether in nature or in your composting operations, all they need is food, energy, oxygen, and water to start thriving. That's pretty standard for most living things.

In a structured composting environment, we endeavor to manage the variables as far as possible. Manageable variables are the ratio of carbon and nitrogen sub-components, airflow, moisture content, and the dispersal of active microbes within the pile. When conditions allow it, microorganisms will immediately start consuming carbon, nitrogen, and oxygen and expelling water vapor and carbon dioxide.

In an environment where microorganisms are active, the oxygen in confined spaces is soon replaced with carbon dioxide (due to carbon respiration). The absence of oxygen will cause microorganisms to become inactive – until they get a fresh oxygen supply. In aerobic composting, oxygen and water need to be continuously replenished. Nitrogen and carbon levels are generally not adjusted. Still, they may be amended to speed up the composting process (nitrogen-rich material added) or manage moisture levels (dry carbon bulking matter added). Excessive moisture levels are commonly indicated by foul odors caused by anaerobic conditions.

Two aeration options that can be used are passive air exchange (natural convection and diffusion) or forced aeration. Personally, I believe that adequate aeration can't be achieved without turning. Pore space in a pile is restored with turning, allowing for better airflow through the materials. The turning process also distributes the microorganisms' population. Importantly, turning provides you with an opportunity to visually review composting conditions in the center of the batch (the activity core).

Temperature is an excellent process indicator because it is directly linked to microbial activity. Within a few hours of building a pile, the temperature rises due to the microbial activity. In most composting situations, the temperature rises rapidly, reaching 120 to 140 degrees Fahrenheit in a matter of hours. Slowly but surely, temperatures begin to drop to 50 degrees Fahrenheit. With every turn, temperatures spike, though each time to a lower peak. As the pile stabilizes, the temperature curve flattens. The temperature pattern changes in response to the rate and type of decomposition (microbial activity).

Peak temperatures are achieved when thermophilic organisms are most active and can reach up to 170 degrees Fahrenheit. A drop in temperature is an indicator that (a) the microbes have run out of oxygen, (b) microbes have run out of food, (c) the pile is too dry for microbial mobility. While some microorganisms might perish in these conditions, others have the means to manage dormancy for as long as 250,000 years.

Piles need to be turned and hydrated if temperatures start dropping. If temperatures go above 140 degrees Fahrenheit, turning helps prevent the pile from reaching temperatures that will destroy fungi populations (and some bacteria). An indicator that the organic material has stabilized is a flattening of the temperature curve after each successive turning.

A consistent temperature indicates the start of the curing phase. The organic matter continues to compost in the curing phase but at a significantly lower rate. The need for oxygen decreases, and turning is no longer required – allowing the compost to be stored. The organic matter continues to break down as the remaining nutrients are consumed by microbes. Compost is considered stable at this point and is ready for application.

COMPOSTING PRODUCTION FACTORS

As seen in the introduction, aerobic hot composting effectiveness depends on the availability of oxygen, compostable organic matter, moisture, the structural characteristics of a pile, particle size, and temperature. We will review the effect of pH as well. Remember my comment that composting is like an orchestra – the symphony emerges when each part complements and helps accentuate the other. At the end of this section, under the heading *Designing an Aerobic Compost Mix,* we will review how the different parts all fit together, each affecting the other. Finally, we will review the management processes to produce stabilized humus loaded with microorganisms and minerals.

Oxygen and Aeration

Oxygen is an essential part of life for us, for microorganisms, and for chemical processes. Composting begins with the breakdown of the most readily available degradable components. As a result, the early stages of the process use oxygen rapidly, and this tapers off towards the end of the process. There is an implication to the early high-oxygen consumption; it means that there will be an equally high respiration rate initially of CO_2 (and other gasses). In a composting pile where aeration is limited, oxygen supply will become unavailable in pockets of the pile. The lack of oxygen will slow the process – until oxygen is supplied. Compost pile pockets must have a constant supply of at least 5% oxygen. Keep in mind that the air we breathe contains only 20.95% oxygen and 78% nitrogen (at sea level). To ensure microorganisms have access to at least 5% oxygen, they need a supply of 25% air.

Anaerobic conditions are indicated by an environment with less than 5% oxygen. Decomposition and biochemical reactions by anaerobic microorganisms are distinctly different from aerobic decomposition. An anaerobic process is generally more time-consuming and less efficient than an aerobic process. Additionally, methane, organic acids, hydrogen sulfide, and other compounds are produced in anaerobic conditions – none of which are sweet-smelling.

In aerobic decomposition, intermediate compounds (organic acids) are briefly formed, but in anaerobic conditions, the intermediate compounds build up. An adequate supply of oxygen gives aerobic organisms an advantage over anaerobic organisms in the competition for resources. In the presence of oxygen, organic acids degrade rapidly. Anaerobic decomposition produces noxious odors if aerobic conditions are not maintained.

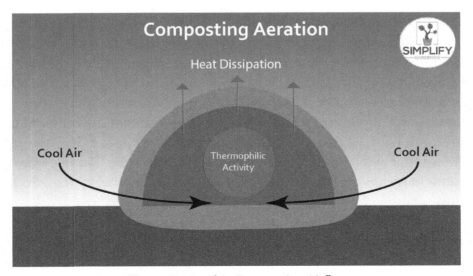

Figure 62: Aerobic Composting Airflow

An additional benefit of aeration is the dissipation of gases trapped within the composting materials, including heat and water vapor. The need for aeration in this process is tiered: the highest need is to dispel heat, followed by the microorganisms' oxygen supply needs, and finally, moisture dissipation. The amount of aeration needed to remove heat can be 10 times greater than the amount of aeration needed to provide microorganisms with oxygen. The frequency of aeration by turning is indicated by rising temperature.

It is therefore essential to constantly monitor the temperatures to determine the peak. Suppose a reading is done after the peak has been reached without you realizing it. In that case, one may assume the temperatures are rising when, in fact, the temperatures are decreasing because the organisms are starving for oxygen. The critical point in measuring temperatures is to monitor the process as temperatures escalate. That way, you will know when to turn the batch to prevent temperatures from going too high or interrupting anaerobic conditions from developing. The peak temperature is also an indicator of conditions within the pile.

We will review the practical implications of aeration at the end of this section. Part of the solution is to manage turning, but the other is how you structure your pile to ensure airflow through the whole pile. We know hot air rises, creating a micro low-pressure system that draws air in from the surrounding surface environment. In constructing our compost pile, we need to keep this in mind. Balancing heat generation, oxygen supply, and water vapor evaporation is the art of composting science.

While aeration is essential, too much air limits the pile's heating potential. Small piles don't heat up specifically because air is too abundant in supply. Like so many important things in life, it's about creating the right environment (atmosphere) and timing. Humor succeeds if the backdrop is executed with a well-timed punchline. It is through the delicate balance of atmosphere and timing that courtship succeeds. If you're too quick in turning, or your pile is too small or too wet, microorganisms will not be active, and temperatures won't rise.

Carbon and Nitrogen and Their Ratio
To flourish, organisms require oxygen (O), carbon (C), nitrogen (N), phosphorous (P), potassium (K), and water (H2O). Certain microbes become more active at higher temperatures, and others have pH-specific needs. The organic compound most abundantly required is carbon.

Carbon is the primary energy source for microorganisms (think of carbohydrates for humans) and is an essential cellular building block (up to 50% of their mass is carbon). Microorganisms use nitrogen for cellular construction and maintenance. Nitrogen is an essential part of proteins, amino acids (think bodybuilders), nucleic acids, and enzymes needed for cell function and growth.

The ideal carbon to nitrogen ratio has been extensively researched. If the *nitrogen levels are too high*, the composting process is fast to start and marked by gaseous emissions (ammonia). Still, it will rapidly run out of carbon, and microbes will perish or become stagnant. Noticeable ammonia losses primarily result from a low C:N ratio. The microorganisms are very efficient at utilizing nitrogen when that is the limiting nutrient. Ammonia's pungent smell indicates excessive nitrogen and lower carbon levels. Nitrogen losses are expected when composting high-nitrogen materials like fresh grass clippings or manure.

Ammonia volatilization is influenced by pH as well. Gaseous ammonia is in equilibrium with water-soluble NH_4+ at about 9.0 pH. Still, higher pH values cause more NH_4+ to be released into the gaseous form, which you can smell. Adding lime to a pile *increases* the ammonia odor because it is less noticeable when the pH is acidic. Fortunately, ammonia is much lighter than air and thus rises quickly.

If carbon levels are too high, there is enough food. Still, the nitrogen required for cellular development will soon become insufficient to support microbe multiplication, and the process will stagnate.

Further, microorganisms use only one-third of the carbon from their consumption of organic matter for cellular growth. The remaining two-thirds of carbon is respired as carbon dioxide ($CO2$). A significant amount of nitrogen can also be lost through gaseous emissions. Still, under well-managed conditions, most of it is used by microorganisms for cellular growth and maintenance. When the organism dies, this consumed nitrogen will be released into the soil system and available to plants. Because of the high loss of carbon to $CO2$, it stands to reason that carbon will be the primary ingredient. Most living organisms, including humans, need about 25 times more carbon than nitrogen for growth and development. Our bodies are 18% carbon and 3% nitrogen.

A C:N ratio of 20:1 to 40:1 is recommended for rapid composting as a starting mix – 30:1 is a safe bet. It is not uncommon to adjust levels incrementally to create a balance between continued organism multiplication and prioritized decomposition while avoiding anaerobic conditions (and odor management). Several life cycles of organisms are required to reduce the C:N ratio to a more suitable level. The end product C:N ratio may be between 10:1 and 15:1.

An essential consideration in compiling your compost pile to contain 30 parts of carbon for every nitrogen part is the substrates' *bioavailability*. Microbial systems only respond to readily available nutrients that they can utilize. A proper C:N ratio and readily available nutrients must be present in the mix of raw materials for microorganisms to thrive. Fruit waste, which contains simple sugars, decomposes quickly. In contrast, woody material, bound by decay-resistant lignins, takes longer to break down. Keratin is the only nitrogen source that is resistant to decay. Keratin is found in various sulfur-containing fibrous proteins that form the chemical basis of epidermal tissue, such as horns, hair, wool, and feathers.

Carbohydrates are the fastest to decompose, followed by hemicellulose and cellulose. In the decomposition of a loofa sponge, the hemicellulose will decompose first, followed by cellulose. The lignin will be the last to decompose.

Moisture

Composting microorganisms need enough water to function without cutting their oxygen supply off. To move and transport nutrients, microorganisms need a thin film of moisture covering the carbon matter. Water is also the medium for chemical reactions. Biological activity is said to be optimal when minerals are saturated.

The ratio of water to organic matter is ideally 55% to 60%. If the moisture level is too high, the oxygen supply is cut off to the microbes. If the mix is too dry, microbes can't function, and the composting process will all but stop.

A practical way of checking moisture levels is to take a fistful of organic material and squeeze it as hard as you can. If you can squeeze out more than a single drop, your batch is too wet. If you're unable to squeeze out a drop, you should hydrate the batch with a light spray of water. The clump from your fist should remain intact when you open your hand but break as soon as you touch it with a finger.

There must be a compromise between ensuring that the microorganisms have enough water to function and keeping oxygen flowing through the compost to maintain aerobic conditions. Microbial activity completely stops at 15% moisture or less. Evaporation and precipitation contribute to changes in the compost pile's moisture content during the composting process. If your compost pile is often exposed to rain, consider ensuring proper drainage. Placing your pile or bin on a pallet is a means to achieving this.

Keep in mind that water vapor is constantly evaporating – a by-product of microbial activity on carbon. You need to monitor moisture constantly and add where needed. If, however, the moisture content of your substrate material is high, then add a dry bulking agent to remedy the situation. You may recall our grass clipping exercise in the previous chapter as an example.

Moisture also serves as a cooling system. The pile's air and material are heated by the composting process. Energy is created as microbes multiply heating up of the contents of the pile. This causes water in the compost pile to evaporate. Suppose there is insufficient moisture in the batch. In that case, the process could generate enough heat to cause the combustion of dry materials. As a fireman, I have attended to several fires at composting facilities. The leading cause of these fires is composting batches that have become too dry. These heaps may smolder and only ignite when oxygen becomes available upon turning the pile.

Controlling pH Levels

The pH scale indicates acidity or alkalinity (also referred to as basicity), where 7.0 is neutral, lower numbers indicate acidity levels, and higher numbers indicate alkalinity. The scale is a logarithm, meaning that each diminishing number is 10 times more acidic than the previous number and vice versa. The pH value is essentially a measure of the concentration of hydrogen ions. The lower the pH value, the higher the hydrogen ion concentration (to the power of 10) and the higher the acidity. This logarithmic feature is also the basis for the pH abbreviation – the power of hydrogen (pH).

Mineral and nutrient solubility is greatly influenced by the pH of the soil. The soil provides 14 of the 17 essential plant nutrients. A nutrient must first be dissolved in the soil solution before being available for plant use. Acidic soils have higher availability and solubility of most minerals and nutrients than neutral or slightly alkaline soils.

Soil with a pH of between 6.0 and 6.5 is the best place to find phosphorus because it is the most readily soluble. Some plants may be harmed by the high-soluble aluminum, iron, and manganese concentrations in highly acidic soils (pH 4.0-5.0). Plant nutrients are most readily available at a pH level of 6.0 to 7.0 (or slightly higher).

Plants like rhododendrons, azaleas, blueberries, potatoes, and conifer trees prefer acidic soils. Some plants, on the other hand, thrive in moderately alkaline soils. By altering the activity of beneficial microorganisms in the soil, the pH of the soil can affect plant growth. Acid soils impede the decomposition of soil organic matter by inhibiting the necessary growth of bacteria. As a result, organic matter accumulates, and nutrients, particularly nitrogen, are locked up in the organic matter.

The composting process is dynamic in that at different phases, pockets in the mix will be either acidic or alkaline at different times. This is because different decomposition activities release varying levels of hydrogen ions. The influence of the pH levels of the raw material used in the compost mix does not significantly impact the composting process, but substrate content does. Between 5.5 and 8.0 is the ideal microbial activity range. Regardless of the starting pH, it will stabilize between 6.0 and 8.0 at the end of the composting process. Even in soil, compost has a pH buffering action.

However, different products and intermediates are produced during the composting process, causing the pH levels to fluctuate. The level of fluctuation depends on the original raw material composition (not pH). Organic acids are formed with high nitrogen availability at the start of the composting process. This is nature's way of ensuring fungi proliferate to consume cellulose and lignin. When the composting process begins, the pH drops to levels of between 4.0 and 5.0 for the first few days. Organic acids can be formed in anaerobic zones, or organic acid intermediates can accumulate due to an abundance of carbonaceous substrates. Bacteria are harmed by acidic conditions, and the composting process is slowed. Eventually, a population of organisms, mostly fungi, will develop using the acidic compounds as a substrate, so composting will continue. The pH rises again as these organisms break down the acidic compounds.

Compost has a built-in buffering capacity, so adjusting the pH is not generally necessary. When nitrogen-rich material is to be composted, higher pH is a concern. Nitrogenous compounds are more readily converted to ammonia at a basic pH (greater than or equal to 8.5). In addition to increasing alkalinity and slowing composting, this ammonia formation promotes nitrogen loss through ammonia volatilization. As a result, the pH may need to be reduced to a value lower than 8.0. The addition of a bulking agent such as sawdust will help.

Acidic conditions in the early stages of composting may necessitate raising the pH, *but rarely*. An appropriate microbial population can begin composting more quickly in acidic conditions because the lag time for an appropriate population to develop is eliminated by a raised pH. Nitrogen losses and ammonia odors increase in alkaline conditions when an additive is used to adjust the pH. In addition to reducing odors, maintaining a pH of 7.0 or lower prevents the formation of organic acid intermediates, which are the source of most the composting site's offensive compounds. My personal advice: let nature do what it does best – leave it be.

Physical Characteristics of Compost Piles

A pile of grass clippings mixed with freshly harvested autumn leaves, even at the proper C:N ratio and considering the moisture levels, will present problems in a compost bin. The reason for this is that the physical characteristics of the mix will not allow sufficient aeration. After starting the process, anaerobic conditions will soon set in, and foul-smelling gasses will be released.

When making compost, you must also consider the physical characteristics of the ingredients. Texture, porosity, and structure are the compost mix's three most important physical characteristics. Aeration, decomposition, and a pile's ability to maintain aerobic conditions are all affected by different physical characteristics.

It is good to have as much surface space as is practically possible in all composting processes. If you make your leaves too fine, room for air (oxygen) movement is reduced. Keeping a balance between particle size and porosity is crucial.

Because the construction of a leaf has evolved to balance weight and efficient light exposure, leaves are generally flat (less so with succulents). Their flat shape creates a mat of leaves that stick to each other when wet, or blows away when dry.

It's a good idea to shred the leaves before adding them to your compost pile. I shred my leaves four times to make them fine enough for my pile. To shred leaves, you can use one of the following methods:

- Run over them with a lawnmower that has a catch-bag. Repeat the process if necessary.
- Vacuum them up with blower-vac – Toro has a good one.
- Put them through a shredder.

To avoid anaerobic conditions, you need air to flow. Grass clippings tend to mat. Because the grass blades are flat and wet (when freshly mowed), they stick to each other and prevent natural airflow.

Porosity measures the amount of air space in the compost mix, affecting how difficult it is for air to flow through the pile. Airflow is restricted if aeration channels are filled with water due to high moisture content. Anaerobic microbial activity dominates as oxygen is prevented from reaching aerobic microorganisms. In the case of the leaves and grass clippings mentioned above, shredding the leaves increases the porosity, surface area, and the ability for air to move through the mass. Adding twigs would further increase porosity.

The trick is finding a balance between small particle sizes for maximum surface area and sufficient substance to ensure desirable airflow. To maximize decomposition, expose as much of the compost particles' surface area as practically possible, and cover those surfaces with a thin layer of water to facilitate microbial action. To maximize aeration, it's vital to create gaps in the mix through which air can move.

The amount of material in the pile that can be decomposed by microorganisms increases when particle size is reduced through methods like selection and grinding. A particle's ability to resist compacting and settling is referred to as structure. Maintaining porosity during the composting process is critical.

Despite having all the necessary components, a mix may not sustain rapid composting if it lacks structure. The composting process slows down if the pile settles and closes off air spaces as the material decomposes. The more absorbent a material is, the more likely it will retain its structure. You will need to manage the composition of your pile to maximize porosity, surface area, and structure equally in the composting process.

Particle Size
When composting fibrous materials like leaves, woody plants, or corn stalks, shredding or grinding is beneficial. Shredding exposes a larger surface area upon which bacteria

can act. Wood and leaves piled together in a compost pile do not decompose quickly because aerobic decomposition cannot proceed as quickly when there is not enough oxygen in the centre of a pile.

The pile becomes aerated, more uniform in size, and easier to wet when the material is shredded. Compost with smaller particles heats more evenly and can withstand more surface drying. Heat loss and water penetration from rain are better prevented by insulating the compost pile. Pulverizing or shredding the material improves fly control as well. It is easier to apply shredded compost to the land because it is more uniform.

Particle size is determined by your requirements for the finished product. However, larger particles can be composted successfully if THEY ARE less than 2 inches of the largest dimension. Compost should be screened through a one-inch screen if it is to be used on lawns or flower gardens because it looks better and is easier to apply and work into the soil.

There are times when shredding a piece of material may not be worth the additional expense and effort. Fork or screen out large particles or break them up if necessary. When it comes to making compost, some people aren't too concerned about the structure of the finished product. For example, uniformity is not as important in agricultural fields as in the home gardener's plot of land.

The initial shredding of all of the material is not required. In many cases, shredding large pieces of organic material is the most efficient method. More oxygen can be trapped in the nooks and crannies created by using larger irregular pieces. When to shred depends on the type of composting raw material. Large, complex feedstocks may necessitate grinding to accelerate degradation. To avoid sogginess, it's best to avoid grinding up vegetation (other than leaves) and herbs. Because of their high moisture content, ground vegetation may cause anaerobic conditions.

Materials can be ground after the compost has matured or near the end of the maturation process. It is possible to grind at the end of the period of active decomposition and leave the pile to stabilize. The type of raw material determines whether to grind or shred it. Consider the final product's appearance, size, and quality. The decomposition process will be sped up by shredding and grinding the materials.

Temperature

Under controlled conditions, the aerobic decomposition of a gram mole of glucose releases 484 to 674 kilo calories (kcal) of energy. In contrast, only 26 kcal is released when it is decomposed anaerobically. If your compost pile has good insulation properties, the released heat increases temperatures within the pile. As some heat loss occurs from the exposed surface, the actual rise in temperature will be slightly less. When the decomposing mass is disturbed, heat loss results in a drop in temperatures during turning. Under adequately controlled conditions, temperatures rise beyond 158 degrees Fahrenheit in aerobic composting. During anaerobic composting, the amount of released heat is relatively small. As part of it is lost from the surface, only a marginal rise in temperature occurs.

The temperature ranges where certain microorganisms thrive have been standardized into subdivisions with unique names. These are not names of microorganisms but merely a way of grouping microbes that typically thrive at given temperatures. Some microbes may function across temperature ranges, and in both aerobic and anaerobic environments – these are referred to as facultative organisms. Our interest lies in the mesophilic and the thermophilic temperature ranges where decomposition occurs. If we get these right, the curing phase in which psychrophilic organisms are active will only require patience. Typically, mesophilic organisms thrive at temperatures between 50 and 105 degrees Fahrenheit. At the higher end of the mesophilic temperatures, thermophilic organisms take over. They could cause the temperature to rise to as high as 180 degrees Fahrenheit. We don't want that to happen.

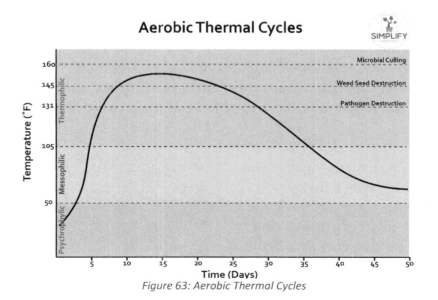

Figure 63: Aerobic Thermal Cycles

Our ideal maximum temperature is in the region of 150 degrees Fahrenheit. At these temperatures, pathogens will be neutralized; weed seeds will be sterilized; and fly larvae, cysts, and eggs of parasites will be destroyed. Also, decomposition is more rapid at these high temperatures. Below 135 degrees Fahrenheit, we run the risk of pathogens surviving. Above 160 degrees Fahrenheit, we run the risk of the compost killing off beneficial microorganisms (especially fungi).

An indication that anaerobic conditions exist in your mix is when the temperatures drop before the compost pile is stabilized. The temperature drops significantly when the pile is anaerobic. If you've got a large compost pile that's been sitting in the sun for a while, the temperature curve will be slightly different. Temperatures can only be maintained in aerobic compost. Expanding the compost pile's volume aids in better heat retention in cold weather. Conversely, reducing its size in warmer weather can assist in limiting the temperature rise.

Compost piles should be at least one cubic yard in size to capitalize on microorganism activity and insulation potentials. Microbial decomposition generates the heat, but insulation (sufficient matter) aids heat retention and the pile's ability to transition from mesophilic to thermophilic temperatures. The rising temperature is possible if the compost pile can provide self-insulating properties. The materials lose heat as the wind carries water vapor and other warm gases away. In managing excessive high temperatures, methods like turning and aeration are employed. The loss of heat is exacerbated by small piles and cold temperatures.

Temperatures above 140 degrees Fahrenheit can rise quickly as the build-up of heat causes a chain reaction where more microorganisms become active. The rising temperature may cause microbial fatalities, slowing the composting process down. This happens when the temperature rises above 160 degrees Fahrenheit because of the continued microbial activity and the insulation properties of composting materials.

Many microorganisms die or go into dormancy at this point. There is no way to restart the process until the population of microorganisms has recovered. The best way to avoid this is to keep an eye on the temperature. At 145 degrees Fahrenheit, turn your

pile immediately. If thermal culling occurs, you can attempt to re-initiate the pile with material from other active batches. Too high temperatures cannot be solved by turning or watering. While this is true, low temperatures will leave pathogens and weed seeds intact. It's a balancing act.

The maximum interior pile temperature is not affected by variations in moisture content between 30% and 60%. There is a direct correlation between moisture levels and the pile's inclination to overheat. When piles are deeper, the temperature rises because the material is exposed to a greater volume of hot air. The mass of the material plays an essential role in maintaining appropriate temperatures.

Time

Several factors influence the time it takes for raw materials to be transformed into compost. It's pretty much a case of "How long is a piece of string." Essentially a regularly agitated, aerated compost pile ought to be stable in three weeks and will take an additional month to fully cure. A rotating drum could compost a small pile in less than a week, though the curing will take about six weeks. Static piles take a bit longer, but we will review that in chapter six.

Regular aeration is critical to speeding up the composting process. Water deficiency and high C:N ratios contribute to a slower growth rate. Due to low temperatures and lack of moisture, in addition to frequent aeration, large particle sizes and high percentages of resistant materials (such as woody materials), slow down the process.

Based on the intended use of the material, the time required for composting varies. Composting time may be shortened if it doesn't need to remain stable. Stability is a product of completing the cycles of microbial tag decomposing. These cycles repeat until the full spectrum of available resources has been depleted, leaving only humus, carbon, microorganisms, and minerals. Stable compost is predictable in its interaction with your soil, and unstable compost will finalize its decomposition in the soil. Extended curing phases ensure remarkably stable compost.

Most materials decompose and stabilize in a few weeks under ideal circumstances, but this is not always the case. Compost can be made in as little as one week in some highly controlled systems, but there's no way to avoid the need to cure for four to eight weeks before being used.

A feigned stabilization can be achieved by drying the materials to a low moisture content, causing microorganisms to become dormant. This is inadvisable because as soon as moisture is available, the microorganisms will again become active – and their behavior in a new environment would be unpredictable (unstable). Some commercial manufacturers wanting to shorten production times are known to do this.

MAKING AN AEROBIC COMPOST MIX

In nature, passive composting takes approximately two years. As soon as the C:N ratio allows and there's enough moisture, spontaneous decomposition happens. Some putrid odors may be released in the process, caused by the absence of available oxygen and anaerobic microorganism activity. In managed composting, nature's part is to recycle organic matter. Our part is to improve efficiency by controlling aeration, moisture levels, substrate composition, and maximum temperatures. In a managed composting process, we can use the generated heat to limit harmful pathogens, weed seeds, and fly larvae.

To achieve a high rate of microbial activity, the design must optimize conditions within the pile for microbial nutrition, oxygen, moisture content, pH, and temperature levels. Three groups of materials are needed: green, brown, and remedial agents. There are no hard-and-fast rules or formulas for creating a composting cocktail. Instead, much of it is trial-and-error from which the gardener or farmer gains experience and develops a *feel*.

Substrates

The fundamental structure of your pile consists of organic material (substrates) that, combined, create a C:N ratio of 30:1. This is achieved by combining carbon-rich materials with nitrogen-rich materials. Carbon-rich materials are often referred to as *brown* material. *Green* material generally refers to fresher organic material with higher nitrogen content. *Remedial agents* could include untreated, dry sawdust, Bokashi inoculant, or, my preference, dried leaf mold. The appendix at the

back of this book contains a comprehensive list of brown and green materials and their C:N ratios.

A good gardening practice is to have a stockpile of dry, shredded leaves or dry sawdust. I emphasize dry because dry matter can help you reduce inherent moisture content – if you need more moisture, just add it. I like to make leaf mold and then dry it out and store it. Adding materials that I know are already populated with microorganisms adds momentum to a waning mix. I use EM-1° for the same purpose – to add microorganisms to my compost batch to help accelerate the process or stabilize it mid-process. I refer to these as my remedial agents. I discuss EM-1 in detail in the fermentation processes section later in this chapter.

In Chapter 4 – Composting Elements, I covered calculating moisture levels and carbon-to-nitrogen ratios in composting substrates. In that example, the substrates were grass clippings and shredded leaves. Let's review another practical example to ground the concept. We'll provide a range of ingredients in this example and find an optimal mix.

Let's look around the yard and see what's available to compost:

- A pile of trimmings from when you cut the California Privet hedge
- A pile of grass clippings
- A bag or two of sawdust in storage
- Some dry branches from last fall's pruning activity
- Lots and lots of fall leaves
- Weeds pulled from the vegetable patch
- Some Swiss Chard that needs to be replaced
- A bag of horse manure

Below is a guideline of the respective material's approximate nitrogen content, their C:N ratios, and their moisture content:

Material	Nitrogen	C:N Ratio	Moisture
Vegetable wastes	2.6%	15:1	85%
Horse manure	1.6%	30:1	55%
Grass clippings	3.0%	17:1	77%
Shrub trimmings	1.0%	54:1	50%
Dry wood	0.1%	500:1	20%
Dry leaves	0.7%	66:1	20%
Pinewood sawdust	0.2%	400:1	5%

Table 62: Common Carbon to Nitrogen Ratios

The percentage of carbon is a product of the percentage of nitrogen and the carbon-to-nitrogen ratio. C + N x (C:N) The formula for calculating the carbon percentage of a material is:

- Vegetable waste carbon is 2.6 x 15 = 39%
- Horse manure carbon is 1.6 x 30 = 48%
- Grass clippings carbon is 3 x 17 = 51%
- Shrub trimmings is 54%
- Dry wood is 50%
- Dry leaves is 46.2%
- Sawdust is 80%

The moisture of any material is the difference in weight between the original wet material and the dry material expressed as a fraction of the wet weight. The formula is:

$$M_n = \left(\left(W_w - W_d \right) \div W_w \right) \times 100$$

Where W_w is the wet weight, and W_d is the dry weight.

Basically, you weigh a small part of the material you're going to include in your compost (wet weight). Pop it in an oven and bake at 212 degrees Fahrenheit for as long as it takes to dry – depending on what *it* is. Now weigh the dry piece and calculate how much moisture was lost in the process (weight loss). Using the formula above, the water lost as a percentage of the original wet weight.

To calculate the C:N ratio for a mix, you need to know the percentages for each substrate's nitrogen, carbon, and moisture levels. Please note that the nitrogen and carbon percentages are their respective representational fraction in dry matter. The sum of nitrogen, carbon, and moisture fractions may therefore be greater than one (>100%).

The best option to manage your mix is to create a spreadsheet with six columns, as shown below:

	A	B	C	D	E	F
1	Ingredient	Weight	% Moisture	% Carbon	% Nitrogen	C:N
2	Vegetable Waste	9	85	39	2.6	15
3	Horse Manure	10	55	48	1.6	30
4	Grass Clippings	7	77	51	3.0	17
5	Shrub Trimmings	2	50	54	1.0	54
6	Dry Wood	2	20	50	0.1	500
7	Dry Leaves	1	20	46.2	0.7	66
8	Pine Sawdust	0	5	80	0.2	400
9					Combined C:N	30.2271

The mathematical formula for the combined C:N ratio is:

$$R = \frac{Q_1\Big(C_1 \times (100 - M_1)\Big) + Q_2\Big(C_2 \times (100 - M_2)\Big) + Q_3\Big(C_3 \times (100 - M_3)\Big) + \dots}{Q_1\Big(N_1 \times (100 - M_1)\Big) + Q_2\Big(N_2 \times (100 - M_2)\Big) + Q_3\Big(N_3 \times (100 - M_3)\Big) + \dots}$$

Where:
Qn = the weight of ingredient n
Nn = the nitrogen percentage in ingredient n
Cn = the carbon percentage in ingredient n
Mn = the moisture content of ingredient n

Using a spreadsheet, the C:N formula in YELLOW is =+D2/E2, and the formula behind the answer in the GREEN F9 cell in is:

=(B2*(D2*(100-C2))+B3*(D3*(100-C3))+B4*(D4*(100-C4))+B5*(D5*(100-C5))+B6*(D6*(100-C6))+B7*(D7*(100-C7))+B8*(D8*(100-C8)))/(B2*(E2*(100-C2))+B3*(E3*(100-C3))+B4*(E4*(100-C4))+B5*(E5*(100-C5))+B6*(E6*(100-C6))+B7*(E7*(100-C7))+B8*(E8*(100-C8)))

The spreadsheet provides you with the means to review your recipe to ensure a 30:1 mix (or as close as possible).

Moisture Content In The Mix

We want to ensure that our mix's moisture content is in the optimal range of 55% to 60%. To calculate the total moisture content, we establish the sum of moisture in all the ingredients and divide it by the total weight we intend to use. The equation for establishing the moisture percentage in a batch is:

$$M_b = \frac{(Q_1 \times M_1) + (Q_2 \times M_2) + (Q_3 \times M_3) + \dots}{Q_1 + Q_2 + Q_3 + \dots}$$

Where:

M_b is the moisture in the batch
Q_n is the added quantity of ingredient n
M_n is the moisture percentage in ingredient n

	A	B	C	D	E	F
1	**Ingredient**	Weight	% Moisture	% Carbon	% Nitrogen	C:N
2	Vegetable Waste	9	85	39	2.6	15
3	Horse Manure	10	55	48	1.6	30
4	Grass Clippings	7	77	51	3.0	17
5	Shrub Trimmings	2	50	54	1.0	54
6	Dry Wood	2	20	50	0.1	500
7	Dry Leaves	1	20	46.2	0.7	66
8	Pine Sawdust	0	5	80	0.2	400
9					Combined C:N	30.2271
10					Moisture Content	64.9677

Using a Spreadsheet, we use the following equation to determine the moisture content in cell F10:

$$=((+B2*C2)+(B3*C3)+(+B4*C4)+(B5*C5)+(B6*C6)+(B7*C7)+(B8*C8))/(B2+B3+B4+B5+B6+B7+B8)$$

Although our batch has the optimal C:N ratio of (almost) 30:1, our inherent moisture in the batch is almost 5% higher than it should be for aerobic conditions. To avoid anaerobic conditions, the moisture levels must remain below 60%. We will need to adjust the ingredients in our mix to balance the C:N ratio and the moisture content. Below is an example where I tried manually to find a better combination. It is more important to get the moisture level between 55% and 60% than to get the carbon to nitrogen exactly on 30:1.

If I have *insufficient* nitrogen, my microorganism farm stock will be slow to multiply. The whole decomposition process will slow. Also, suppose I add a compost batch with high carbon to my soil. In that case, the organisms will grab the nitrogen from the surrounding area, and less will be available to plants. On the other hand, high nitrogen levels will boost my microorganism farm stock but deplete my carbon matter. When the carbon is depleted, the microorganisms will become latent or even perish. High nitrogen batches produce ammonia gas, depleting available nitrogen for soil benefits. Keeping your C:N ratio between 24 and 40 is acceptable. The higher nitrogen (lower ratio) is primarily a factor when wet composting manures. Lower nitrogen (higher ratios) is most suitable for aerobic composting. With aerobic composting, always aim for a carbon ratio of between 30 and 40.

	A	B	C	D	E	F
1	Ingredient	Weight	% Moisture	% Carbon	% Nitrogen	C:N
2	Vegetable Waste	10	85	39	2.6	15
3	Horse Manure	10	55	48	1.6	30
4	Grass Clippings	10	77	51	3.0	17
5	Shrub Trimmings	6	50	54	1.0	54
6	Dry Wood	3	20	50	0.1	500
7	Dry Leaves	5	20	46.2	0.7	66
8	Pine Sawdust	0	5	80	0.2	400
9					Combined C:N	35.7155
10					Moisture Content	59.7727

The above mix will work well – its moisture content is below 60%, and the carbon content is close to the middle of 30 and 40. Ideally, you want it closer to 30:1. Here's a way to solve the problem for those pedantic about these things – with an Excel add-in called Solver.

	A	B	C	D	E	F
1	**Ingredient**	**Weight**	**% Moisture**	**% Carbon**	**% Nitrogen**	**C:N**
2	Vegetable Waste	1.211388	85	39	2.6	15
3	Horse Manure	10	55	48	1.6	30
4	Grass Clippings	10	77	51	3.0	17
5	Shrub Trimmings	1.715731	50	54	1.0	54
6	Dry Wood	0.521885	20	50	0.1	500
7	Dry Leaves	2.806299	20	46.2	0.7	66
8	Pine Sawdust	0	5	80	0.2	400
9	Combined C:N					30
10	Moisture Content					60

Solver is a Microsoft Excel add-in program available when installing Microsoft Office or Excel. To use the Solver add-in, you first need to load it in Excel.

- In Excel, go to File and select Options
- Click Add-Ins, and in the Manage box, select Excel Add-ins
- Click Go
- In the Add-Ins available box, select the Solver Add-in check box, and then click OK

If the Solver add-in is not listed in the Add-Ins Available box, click Browse to locate the add-in. If prompted that the Solver add-in is not currently installed on your machine, click Yes to install it.

After you load the Solver add-in, the Solver command is available in the **Data** tab in the **Analysis** group. (In newer versions, the name Solver doesn't appear, but a symbol for the app does.) You may need to restart Excel before it is available.

Solver helps solve complex quantitative problems – like getting a precise composting recipe that meets several conditions. The principle is that you provide the app with an objective (a cell that contains a formula) and point it to the range of variables that need to change to realize the objective.

In the Solver dialogue box, we specify the set objective. The objective is for the formula in cell F9 to return a value of 30. The variables that can be changed to achieve this are in column B – the weights of each ingredient. We also want the moisture to be less than 60%. We define this requirement as a constraint. Basically, we're telling the app to give us a 30:1 C:N ratio by manipulating the quantity of each ingredient. However, while calculating that, the app is constrained to give answers that also satisfy the need for cell F10 to be equal to, or lesser than, 60. Right?

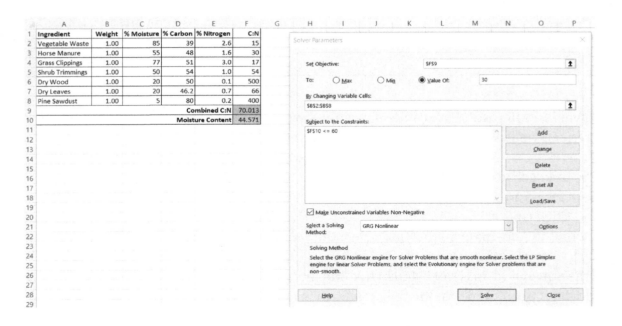

To help avoid zero division errors, let's start with one pound of each of the seven ingredients. In cell F9, we have the formula for calculating the C:N ratio. The formula references the specifications of each ingredient and their mass or representative percentages – weight, moisture, carbon, and nitrogen. In cell F10, we have the formula for the combined moisture content. Both these formulas are given above. We only want to change column B – the quantities by weight. The moisture, carbon, and nitrogen percentages are established and fixed.

With one part of each of the seven ingredients, the C:N ratio is a whopping 70:1, and the moisture content is a low 44.5%. This is before we have instructed Solver to solve. Let's run it – press the *Solve* button at the bottom.

Great, it works! We know that a batch should be at least a cubic yard in size – 3 foot square and 3 foot high. Six pounds of organic matter is hardly enough. Let's boost the volume. The grass clippings ingredient is the one that won't keep – and we have 10 pounds of it. Let's instruct *Solver* to use all our available grass clippings and see how that affects the rest of the batch. We do this by adding an additional *Subject to Constraints* statement – grass clippings equal 10.

Click the Add button to the right of that dialogue box and a small new dialogue box pops up. In the left input block, point to cell B4 (Grass clippings quantity). Select the condition in the middle from the drop-down menu (=). In the right input block, specify 10. Remember to click OK – if you click add, you can add more constraints. Solve!

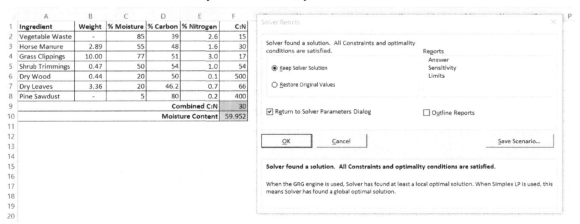

Brilliant. Let's see what Solver decided for us. First, let's review the previous minimum batch's data. Remember that both met the Solver requirements for C:N ratios (30:1) and moisture content of 60%.

Ingredient	Original Weight	Revised Weight	% Moisture	% Carbon	% Nitrogen
Vegetable Waste	0.66	-	85	39	2.6
Horse Manure	2.13	2.89	55	48	1.6
Grass Clippings	2.06	10.00	77	51	3.0
Shrub Trimmings	0.25	0.47	50	54	1.0
Dry Wood	-	0.44	20	50	0.1
Dry Leaves	0.96	3.36	20	46.2	0.7
Pine Sawdust	-	-	5	80	0.2
TOTAL	6.06	17.15			

The addition of the 10 pounds of grass clipping influenced both the moisture and nitrogen levels – increasing both. Of all the materials, the grass clippings ingredient has the highest nitrogen levels (one of the reasons why leaving clippings on the lawn will cut your fertilizer bill). Additionally, it's the second-most moist ingredient. It's no wonder then that the vegetable waste was left out. To deal with the moisture challenge and buffer the high nitrogen, the offered solution is tripling the weight of the leaves. Intelligent machine.

By adding additional constraints, like using at least a specific weight of an ingredient, Solver will suggest a revised optimal mix. These are very helpful for guidelines, and with time you will develop a sense of what works and what doesn't.

Bulking Agents

In some cases, the C:N ratio and the moisture content can't be adequately balanced with the available material. Ideally, the C:N ratio and/or moisture content should be designed to fall within the recommended ranges, with the latter as close to the ideal as possible. The type of material and the composting method influence which of the two criteria, C:N ratio or moisture content, must be met. There are times when both C:N ratio and moisture content can't be balanced, and the compost mix is proportioned accordingly. Compost that is too wet has a more significant impact on the composting process than a dry mix.

The composting process is halted if the moisture content is too low (below 15%) or too high (more than 60%). Foul odors are a sign of anaerobic conditions that may have been caused by high moisture content in the compost mix. A C:N ratio below the recommended range (high nitrogen) results in ammonia volatilization, which causes odors and nutrient losses. Calculations alone should not be used to determine the correct compost mix.

Mix proportions (recipes) may be affected by the material's water absorption, degradability, and structure, as well as other intangibles. It is possible to have the correct C:N ratio and moisture content, yet if the carbon isn't available or the porosity isn't adequate, the mix will not compost properly. Composting recipes can be developed using calculations, but only through hands-on experience can one learn which materials compost best and in what proportions.

When working with volumes of wetter composting ingredients, bulking agents become essential for maintaining a healthy environment. Commonly, bulking agents are shredded leaves, wood shavings, and any material that adds texture, absorbs moisture, and ensures an aerobic environment. These items should be collected throughout the year – shredded, dried, and stored. Shredded leaves have a multitude of uses in gardening.

I'm thinking of grass clippings, weeds, vegetable waste, and food scraps when referring to wetter ingredients. I have a farmer friend locally that allows me to collect horse manure annually. The stock I take is generally drier. I get other manure from my hens. I collect this with the bedding stock (wood shavings), so it doesn't require an additional bulking agent when composting.

If you're adding food waste to your compost bin, ensure that it's covered with a bulking agent. While it aids in controlling the high moisture, it also helps prevent rodent and scavenger problems. Personally, my food scraps go to my chickens, and the rest I ferment with the help of effective microorganisms (EM®) in my Bokashi Bin. That way, rats and other vermin are hardly ever a problem.

Just a note here. While horse manure is a good source of raw material, it can be troublesome. Non-compostable material is common in manure from racetracks and barns of show horses. Highly prized animals are often treated with antibacterial and antibiotic substances that make their excrement unsuitable for composting purposes.

Additions may be necessary if the moisture and C:N ratios cannot be achieved with only two ingredients. This will necessitate a more significant number of computations. Degradability, porosity, structure, rainfall, climate, and C:N and moisture losses must all be considered in addition to the target C:N ratio. The carbonaceous material in a compost pile decomposes and is released into the atmosphere as carbon dioxide (CO_2), while nitrogen is retained. A smaller amount of nitrogen is lost through volatilization, leaching, or denitrification.

The amount of moisture in a pile also decreases throughout the composting process because of evaporation; the amount of water lost from a compost pile is greater than the amount added by rain. While extreme wet and cold weather can lead to a net water gain, this is not always the case. I cover my pile in heavy rain. Because the compost mix's moisture content and C:N ratio are likely to decrease during the process, set them to the upper end of the acceptable range (60% moisture and a 30:1 carbon-to-nitrogen ratio) to start with. If your pile is aerated, the composting process will keep them in check in the recommended ranges.

Remedial Additions

If you follow me on YouTube on the Simplify Gardening channel, you'll notice that I'm transparent regarding my failures. As any honest gardener will tell you, we celebrate our success, always realizing that a variation in a single element could scupper our efforts. In gardening, even the best laid out plans can go awry. Nature has a way of teaching us all that she needs to be approached with humility. One year your methods produce great results – the next, the same methods fail to provide a return. That's gardening.

The skilled gardener has learned tricks that *mostly* work, either from others or trial-and-error. In composting, there are several things you can do to salvage a batch that is heading in an unintended direction. Three of the most common challenges with composting batches are:

- Anaerobic conditions evidenced by a release of foul odors
- Failure to start evidenced by temperatures in the batch not rising within the first three days
- The presence of rodents and other scavengers

Managing Anaerobic Conditions

Let's consider each of these in turn. **Anaerobic conditions** prevail when oxygen is unable to keep aerobic microorganisms active. Fungi, for instance, are predominantly aerobic. You need your fungal population to remain intact and abundant for any material with high cellulose (straw) or lignin (wood and leaves) content. This is especially the case in the early stages of decomposition.

Both bacteria and fungi have the potential to digest cellulose. On the other hand, some fungi have enzymes that degrade lignin-covered cellulose. Up to 100 times more effective than bacteria's enzymes, these enzymes can break down peptide bonds. The anaerobic condition slows the bacterial degradation of cellulose even further.

The most common cause of early-stage anaerobic conditions is excessive moisture in a batch. Remember that your batch must not be wet, merely damp. Your composting material must be uniformly covered in a thin layer of water. Only when tightly pressed should substrates release a drop of water. If your batch is too moist, oxygen cannot get to the fungi needed to break the cellulose and lignin down. The decimated carbon material then becomes available for bacteria for further decomposition. Many of the fungi initially thought to be obligatory aerobic are facultatively anaerobic. This means that they function well in an aerobic environment but adapt to anaerobic conditions when necessary. Anaerobic bacteria step up and take over the decomposition process in anaerobic conditions. They break complex material down to sulfur, nitrogen, and volatile fatty acids.

One of my preferred ways of reducing water content in a batch while dealing with anaerobic conditions simultaneously is adding shredded leaves – but with a twist. By adding leaf mold, I provide the environment with a highly hygroscopic (water-attracting and retaining) substance *and* boost the microbial population. Most of the carbon in leaf mold has already been decomposed, so it hardly affects the C:N ratio. The fungi-rich material boosts microbial activity and accelerates the decomposition of lignin-rich material in the batch (wood and leaves). We cover the production of leaf mold later in this chapter.

Failure to Start

It happens to the best of us. The moisture challenge forces us to add brown dryer material, pushing the C:N ratio up. We know that of all the controllable factors, moisture control is essential. We manage to balance the moisture content in our batch by upping the C:N ratio closer to 40:1 – and nothing happens. No matter where we poke our composting thermometer, the reading hardly changes – an indicator of little or no microorganism activity.

Compost pile temperatures do not reach thermophilic levels for several days after the composting period begins. During this time, the microbial population should grow, and the scale of activity will increase. If the lag is longer than a week or your batch has become developmentally stunted, additives may be a solution. Additives, also called inoculum, are a concentration of microbes and enzymes, and our leaf mold above is an example.

The C:N ratio, pH, or humidity can be controlled by adding additives to the initial mixture. I included a liquid mixture (tea) of horse manure, urine, and forest floor soil in my YouTube video on leaf mold production. This is an example of an inoculum – a combination of microbes from the wooded area, nitrogen in uric acid, and horse manure.

Though not essential, adding inoculums to compost increases the efficacy of the process, at least in theory. An initial compost mix with a high concentration of enzymes and microorganisms should immediately initiate microbial activity, and decomposition should follow suit. In theory, compost pile decomposition may be aided by the addition of beneficial microorganisms and enzymes. The increased efficiency and resulting thoroughness should benefit both the final product and the environment.

While the above is theoretically accurate, it remains an interruption of a natural process. Interrupting nature or coaxing her in a specific direction can have unforeseen outcomes. The differences between theory and reality are significant because of the complex processes and microbial populations within each compost pile. Inoculum that doesn't accurately represent the microbial population that makes composting possible in the first place can have the opposite effect. A use for inoculums is to supply the compost with microorganisms that aren't already there, or increase the already existing population, i.e., to manipulate microbial life in the compost mix.

The truth is that our interventions are often based on assumptions. Accurately determining these requirements is extremely difficult because of compost's constantly changing microbial environment. The inoculum may not be as effective as expected because the internal environment is in constant flux. The microbial activity in a batch constantly evolves in response to an ever-changing environment. Newly introduced microorganisms may not be as well-suited to the waste's conditions as the native microbial population. During the composting process, various substrates and environmental conditions influence the growth of microbial populations.

This can lead to a less-than-optimal performance from the microbial population inoculated into the pile. Inoculums and starters also contain enzymes, which break down the organic matter in the compost mix over time. Because of their specificity and sensitivity to environmental conditions, such as temperature fluctuations, enzymes are even more challenging to identify. At higher temperatures, enzymes denature.

Additional materials can be added to the initial compost mix to adjust its C:N ratio, moisture levels or pH, and control odors. I'm not a fan of adding synthetic fertilizers such as nitrogen. In my opinion, urea in a natural form is a better option. Concentrated nitrogen sources can have an adverse effect on C:N ratios because nitrogen can be available more quickly than organic carbon. This will cause nitrogen loss as ammonia gas or leached from the pile.

The suppliers of starters make a variety of claims. These claims cannot be verified without knowing the unique microbial activity in your batch. Inoculating one pile and using a control pile as a determinant is the best way to test the starter's efficacy. If the starter performs as claimed, the results of the composition of each pile are then compared. The debate over whether inoculums or enzymes improve the composting process is ongoing.

In my experience, staying as close to natural processes as possible is a healthier approach. The addition of leaf mold, samples of soils I want to emulate, and EM° effective microorganisms have helped me solve no-start batches. I cover the use of EM for fermentation of kitchen scraps in a later chapter. In this book and in my Composting Masterclass Course, I give enough information for you to make an informed decision.

My advice is to delay using starters until their use is imperative to success. Nature has a way of solving her own challenges. We may not like her response, but it may be better to change the environment than introduce added complexity. This applies to our personal lives too. Every batch of compost is different, influenced by composition, weather conditions, latent microbial life, and structure of the batch. The required response to any challenge needs to be as unique as the challenge. You will find that experience in your context is the best possible situational teacher.

Managing Pests and Scavengers

Most authors will advise against including certain products in a composting mix. Products such as meat, fats, and cow's milk products are known to attract rodents and scavengers. Excluding them from the batch is probably the best option. However, there are ways to include them in composting without initiating a plague.

Foods that are generally excluded from composting batches:

- ✗ Butter
- ✗ Bones
- ✗ Cheese
- ✗ Chicken
- ✗ Fish scraps
- ✗ Lard
- ✗ Mayonnaise
- ✗ Meat scraps
- ✗ Milk products

✗ Peanut butter
✗ Salad dressing
✗ Vegetable oils
✗ Yogurt

Disease-carrying rats and other wildlife can deposit urine and feces on fruit, vegetables, and the soil. Fruits and vegetables can also be harmed by rats, who can eat the produce or gnaw on it, making it unsuitable for human consumption. As they burrow, Norway rats put beds and root systems at risk. While rats can damage drip irrigation tubes by chewing on them, other animals more commonly do so.

Many rodents can be kept at bay simply by removing their food supply. But it would be counter-intuitive to remove food from a garden because the primary purpose is to grow food. People who work in gardens to protect their food from rat damage have many options.

Keeping your garden's landscape in good condition may help keep rats at bay. Rats can find a lot of shelter in the form of landscaped shrubs, trees, and untrimmed palm trees, to mention but a few. These should be trimmed up and off the ground, and they should not be overly densely planted. You should avoid composting food near your garden because it provides rats with a great place to hide. To prevent rat colonies from forming in compost piles, ensure that all other green waste is regularly removed.

Odor control and rodent control are critical considerations for community composting, especially in urban areas. Although closed systems, such as rotating drums and small tumblers, generally have an advantage over open ones regarding odor control and rodent proofing, good management remains essential for all systems.

As a result of their open design, rodents have no difficulty getting into open piles. However, rodents are less interested in a well-built pile that meticulously incorporates any food into the pile before being then sealed to a depth of at least 6 inches. Well-constructed piles can be rodent proof if they are appropriately placed with open space all around that would deter rodents from using the pile as a habitat. Rodents seek food, warmth, and safety. Increased foot traffic, activity around the pile, and open spaces are effective deterrents.

Rodents are difficult to deal with because they can gnaw through wood and plastic. Even if they cannot get to the food, they may take residence under the bin/container. Bins, including the top hatch, require a full wrap of at least a 12-inch hardware cloth to prevent food access (rats will climb the sides to get in through the top). The bin's base needs a barrier to keep rodents from creating a habitat there during the cold climate winters (like cement, a dug-out pit with sand, or something else inhospitable). Tumblers that are rodent-proof and easier to use may be more cost-effective than plastic containers, which can still be chewed on by rats.

If food products have been fermented and decomposed using a process like Bokashi, their inclusion does not attract rodents. Also, using Bokashi that has been incorporated into the soil for two weeks can significantly enhance the microorganism population of a batch.

AEROBIC HOME COMPOSTING TECHNIQUES

Below are the most common aerobic composting techniques. The listed personalized technique is equally acceptable. The list aims to create a point of reference to the various adaptations and their effect on the quality of the final product.

Method	Features			
	Particle Size Management	**Turning Intervals**	**Inoculation**	**Duration**
Indore Heap Composting	Shredded	Every 6 weeks	Previous compost	3 months
Berkeley Rapid Composting	Shredded Finely	Daily or alternate day turning		4 to 6 weeks
Simplify Gardening Composting	Shredded	Weekly for the first 2 weeks and then fortnightly	Leaf Mold	4 to 8 weeks

Table 63: Popular Aerobic Composting Techniques

Indore Heap

In reviewing this process, we explore the work of one of the prominent pioneers of Western composting methods. Some of today's techniques are strongly linked to the Indore heap principles.

Even though farmers and gardeners of the nineteenth century had a good deal of practical knowledge about using animal wastes as fertilizer, little was known about the actual microbial process of composting. Sir Albert Howard, a brilliant composter, incorporated the new science of soil microbiology into his composting and, through patient experimentation, learned how to make superior compost.

As history goes, Sir Albert Howard was in charge of a UK government research farm in Indore, India, in the 1920s. As a committed altruist, Howard wanted to increase sustainable productivity within the context of India in the early twentieth century. Surrounding farms were producing cotton, sugar cane, and a variety of grains using oxen. The idea was to improve the health of the soil that was noticeably low in organic matter.

Using the farm's waste, Howard developed a method to produce enough high-quality fertilizer for the entire operation. This research farm soon had record yields without insect or disease problems or purchasing commercial fertilizer or seed. It was a great success. Indore's humus-rich soil produced fodder that helped boost the grazing stock immune system. This prompted interest from local farmers.

Trial and error, mixed with perseverance, resulted in eventual success. Aside from preserving the nitrogen in cattle manure and crop waste, Howard demonstrated that his method conserved land-produced organic matter and raised the entire operation to an ecological pinnacle. Healthier soil produced healthier crops, resulting in healthier animals and people. This cycle repeats itself – invest in soil health, and the produce from the soil returns to increase the soil's fertility even further.

Howard's success at rising net nitrates was a quantum leap at the time. This has revolutionized agriculture ever since. Farm soils became more humus-rich, and no nitrogen or organic matter was lost in his technique. Nitrate nitrogen levels in the finished compost were higher than those in the materials that formed it.

In 1931, Howard's book, *The Waste Products of Agriculture*, details the Indore method. The book's publication stimulated global interest – and the composting movement was born (in the West, at least). Howard is said to have been quite pedantic, asserting that his way had been tested and shown to be the best way. I lift my hat in a salute, Sir Albert Howard – well done on birthing the concept of what is globally known as the Indore Composting process – enriching soil without the use of chemicals.

Howard used every available resource he had. This included manure and bedding straw from the cattle sheds, unconsumed crops, fallen leaves, other forest wastes, and weeds and green manures grown specifically for compost making. The climate in Indore, India, allowed for year-round composting. It's interesting to note that Howard's primary source of "nitrifying power" was leaf mold.

Howard emphasized that the carbon-to-nitrogen ratio of the material entering the heap must always be in the same range for the Indore method to work consistently. Every time a heap was constructed, the same mixture of crop wastes, fresh manure, and urine earth was added. Howard ensured the consistency of the ingredients.

This constituted a layer of carbonaceous material 8 inches thick, followed by a 4 inch layer of green material. The same pattern is followed until a height of 5 foot, i.e., five layers of each. The Indore process starts from a base of 5x5 feet and tapers to a height of about 5 feet. The top layer is a 3x3 foot square. That was on a farm – in a backyard compost pile, a 3 foot square base will be the minimum size to retain the heat. Some operations cover the pile with straw to help heat retention.

A unique feature of the technique is how Howard dealt with insufficient nitrogen-rich green materials. After the first turning, he sowed green manure or leguminous crops on the fermenting heap. After it has grown, the green matter is turned into the pile, and the pile is only turned every six weeks.

Howard was a strong advocate for shredding material. Apparently, he covered the road with carbon-rich material for carts to ride over and oxen to tread. Howard was also the first to recognize the need to measure temperature thresholds. According to his recording, he regularly reached 140 degrees Fahrenheit on his first turning and 125 degrees Fahrenheit on the second.

Howard was able to "bank the fires" of decomposition by restricting the air supply and thereby build up the thermal mass. His key to preventing the loss of nitrogen was this moderation of air supply. The piles were watered as needed, rotated several times, and inoculated with the appropriate fungi and bacteria in a novel mass inoculation method.

A large amount of biologically active material from older compost heaps was incorporated into Howard's current batch of compost to speed up and direct decomposition. As a result of his method, many of the most beneficial microorganisms could establish significant populations before less desirable ones could do so. A similar strategy has been used before by brewers, winemakers, and bread makers worldwide. In fact, there's a "safe" in Belgium that houses a sample of all the world's most famous sourdough bread starters.

The material was incorporated into the soil when the C:N ratio was low enough to preserve nitrate nitrogen. However, the soil cannot break down raw organic matter while simultaneously converting humus into nitrate. According to Howard, when compost is tilled in, it must be completely cured and ready to use.

Berkeley Rapid Composting

Compostable material should not be larger than 1.5 inches in diameter. Because they decompose so quickly, soft, succulent tissues don't need to be chopped up. Leaves, however, should be shredded. To speed up the decomposition of hard or woody tissues, they must be broken down into smaller pieces. Most grinders chop herbaceous material too finely for effective composting, so only grind woody materials. Using a sharp shovel to chop up the material works well. This is a time-consuming exercise but focusing on the benefits of physical exercise and the anticipation of quality compost makes the effort worthwhile.

The end composition of compostable materials should have a carbon to nitrogen ratio of 30:1 to function optimally during the composting process. In addition to fresh garbage, fruit and vegetable waste is another type of green material used in composting. Dead leaves, dried grass, straw, and somewhat woody pruning materials are all examples of dried material. Fall and early spring are the best times to find these kinds of resources, but once the growing season begins, they become more challenging to come by.

It is acceptable to use finely chopped or shredded cardboard boxes, cereal boxes, and milk cartons for dried materials during this period. It is possible to use newspapers if they are shredded and separated by plant tissues so that they do not mat. Matting is undesirable because oxygen is required for rapid decomposition, and matting excludes this oxygen. The term "green" refers to any cut green material, even if allowed to dry. Grass clippings and other green materials, such as leaves, can clump together if they aren't separated by dry materials. Shred leaves with a shredder or lawnmower at least four times until they are relatively fine.

Materials in the compost pile should have a moisture content of about 55%. With practice, it is possible to estimate the correct amount of moisture. Decomposition will be slow and smelly if there is too much moisture in the mass. Slow or no decomposition will occur if the organic material is too dry.

The microorganisms' respiration as they break down organic materials provides the heat needed for rapid composting. A minimum of 36 cubic feet of material is required to keep heat from escaping and build up the necessary temperature. That is 3 foot square and 3 foot high. Smaller piles will only work if the ambient temperature is high. A slightly bigger pile will help in colder weather.

Faster composting can be achieved if bins are used rather than open piles, as heat retention is better in bins. It's also a lot nicer to use bins. When the temperature rises above 160 degrees Fahrenheit, the fastest-decomposing microorganisms thrive, and a healthy pile will stay at or near that temperature. A thermometer is helpful but not essential in determining the pile's temperature.

To avoid the compost pile becoming too hot, it is necessary to turn it regularly. Microbes will die if the temperature rises above 160 degrees Fahrenheit, and the entire process will have to be restarted. To keep the most active decomposers active, it is necessary to rotate the pile and keep it aerated. Material on the outer edges of the pile should be shifted toward the center. Each piece of material will reach its ideal temperature at a different point in time. Since heat is lost along its edges, the pile's optimal temperature can be found only in the center. To facilitate turning, two bins are needed to transfer material between them. Bins with removable slats in the front make it easier to turn. Bins with covers are better at retaining heat than bins without covers.

When the decomposition process begins, the pile shrinks, and some heat is lost at the top because the bin is no longer full. Using a polyethylene plastic sheet slightly larger than the top of the bins will prevent this. Immediately after the compost has been turned, plastic is placed directly on top of it, tucked in around the perimeter.

Composting will take two weeks or a little longer if the pile is turned *daily*, and it will take about three weeks to complete if rotated every other day. For the composting process to be fast, daily turning is required.

Don't make any additions after the batch has started heating (with perhaps one exception, which will be mentioned in chapter nine). Your slowest decomposer sets the rate of the whole batch. Adding fresh material to the batch is the same as restarting the process. When storing excess materials, they should be kept as dry as possible until the start of a new pile. The compost pile's efficacy will be compromised if you add material that is only partially decomposed in a separate process.

Organic materials decompose without the need for any additional ingredients. Compost piles are a perfect breeding ground for the microorganisms involved in decomposition, which can be found virtually anywhere plant material is present.

A pile can reach high temperatures in 24 to 48 hours if constructed correctly. A lack of green material (or nitrogen) or an excessively wet or dry pile are the most likely causes. If the material is excessively wet, it should be spread out to dry as soon as possible. Add water if the batch is too dry. If adjusting the moisture content does not produce the desired results, the non-start is due to a lack of nitrogen. By adding grass clippings, fresh chicken manure, ammonium sulfate, or a one to five dilution of urine ought to get the process kickstarted.

Decomposition of organic matter occurs much more rapidly, but nitrogen is lost if the C:N ratio is less than 30:1 (more nitrogen). The smell of ammonia is a telltale sign. High-carbon sawdust can be added to the pile to counteract the ammonia odor. This is the only thing that should be added to a pile once it has started – and water if it gets too dry. Covering the composting pile during the rainy season may be necessary to keep the materials from becoming too wet.

Soil, fireplace ashes, and feces from carnivorous animals should not be added to a composting pile. In a compost pile, soil does nothing but add weight and makes turning the pile more laborious. Composter piles and soils with a pH of less than 6.5 should not have wood ashes added to them. Use only manures from herbivorous animals, such as rabbits, goats, cattle, horses, elephants, or fowl.

The pleasant smell in stable, healthy compost is caused by actinomycetes. Other indicators of a successful batch are the heat produced, the growth of white fungi on the decomposing organic material, a reduction in volume, and a change in the color of the materials to dark brown. It gets cooler as composting progresses until there is little or no heat left at all. After that, the compost can be put to use. Screening the material through a 1 inch mesh chicken wire will keep large pieces out of the compost if they weren't chopped up small enough during the composting process. Decompose them by adding them to the next pile.

Simplify Gardening Composting

I use a three-bin system that is made from covered wooden pallets. Two bins would work, too, if you plan to bag the completed compost. The first bin is where I start the process, the second bin is empty, and the third bin has compost that is almost ready for use (in the final curing stage). The fronts of  the bins are open but can be closed using slats that slide in from the top. We'll explore the details of the structures and vessels used in composting later in chapter six.

Shredded substrates increase the surface area microorganisms can act on. Guard against compaction and anaerobic conditions by alternating the particle sizes included. I keep stock of dry brown material and leaf compost when green material becomes available. When compiling your batch, include some material that can provide some structure. These could be thinner twigs and weed stems that aren't too thick. When I prune my trees, I always keep my composting process in mind.

You can ensure a 30:1 C:N mix by structuring the pile in layers of two parts carbon-rich brown material and one part nitrogen-rich green material. My bins are 4 foot cubes – the width of a pallet, and I fill them to overflowing as there is a 50% reduction in volume (and mass) in the composting process. At the bottom, I add carbon material that provides some aeration – branches and twigs and shredded leaves.

My layers are 4 inches of brown material, an inch-thick layer of leaf mold, and a topping of 2 inches of green material. I repeat the process until the bin is full to overflowing – as much as I can fit without compacting it, especially with a fresh batch. Although I used to calculate my C:N ratio, I find that the above ratios provide the required 30:1 C:N ratio. I add the leaf mold to aid in breaking down the cellulose and lignin in the carbon matter. This added processing capacity ceases to be available once a temperature of 160 degrees Fahrenheit is reached – the temperature at which most fungi become inactive. From then on, only bacteria and actinomycetes are active. Fungi become active again when the temperature drops below 160 degrees Fahrenheit.

Materials in the compost pile should be damp – not soggy. Remember, it is easier to add water than remove it. With practice, it is possible to estimate the correct amount of moisture. Decomposition will be slow and smelly if there is too much moisture in the mass. Slow or no decomposition will occur if the organic material is too dry (less than 30% moisture)

I use a closed system to control the amount of air that comes into my batch. The area I live in has significant temperature fluctuations and high rainfall, and controlling heat loss is essential. As the microorganisms become active, the temperature rises, carbon dioxide is expelled, and the pH drops. I watch my  temperatures to ensure we don't go over 150 degrees Fahrenheit at the center of the pile.

My bins are relatively large (4 foot cubed), so temperatures can rise fast. In addition, I cover the top of my batch with a black plastic sheet during the day and a white sheet during the night. The color black absorbs all the colors of light and emits heat. White emits little heat and is a better insulator when no light is available.

It is easier to reconstruct your substrates in an open pile so that what was on the outside ends in the middle of the new pile, and vice versa, after each turning. In a closed (or partially closed) system like the three-bin system, the peripheral material is removed onto the ground, enabling you to get to the core. The core material is then used to line the outer edges of the bin before placing the fresher matter in the center and covering it with composted material. This is the reason for having a second bin.

Adding material to the soil that is still rich in organic carbon matter causes the microorganisms in the soil to flourish. You need microorganism mortalities for the nitrogen to be released to the plants. Making sure that all the material in the batch is fully exposed to thermophilic microorganism action makes a compost batch stable. Each material part must be broken down by thermophilic microorganisms to remove any pathogens and weed seeds, becoming stabilized in the process.

I have no fixed schedule for turning but am instead informed by the temperature readings I get. As soon as the batch gets to 145 degrees Fahrenheit, I start turning the pile. Remember this is the minimum temperature at which turning can take place as this is the temperature required for neutralizing seeds (including weed seeds).

Once the process has started, I make no additions. If I detect the smell of ammonium, I may add some dried leaf mold. Wait a while before doing this, however, because some ammonia is released in the early stages but will stabilize as soon as the readily available nitrogen has been consumed.

The first high peak is typically reached within two to three days. I make sure to include some grass clippings, though I prefer to leave my clipping on the lawn for the nitrogen benefits. I keep some purely for composting as it helps kickstart a pile. I also make a compost tea – a mix of diluted urine (1:5), in which I soak a bag of chicken manure and compost from a previous batch. I use this solution to wet my pile as I construct it. It is easier to provide the fuel before you start than incorporate it in the batch once you have layered everything.

I log my temperatures for each batch and record the quantities of the substrates I use. This helps me learn what works when and how. Some batches rocket to high temperatures, smell fabulous throughout the process, produce dark-brown humus, and cause my garden to flourish. Other batches are less successful. Both success and failure are part of learning, and learning never stops. Every variation in organic matter used, weather conditions, and invisible factors contribute to the outcome. We try our best, and nature does the rest.

STATIC PILE AEROBIC COMPOSTING

The differentiating adjective for this form of composting is static instead of moving. Static piles are not moved from one bin to the next in the turning process, and that is because there is no turning of the pile. The lower part of the pile is harvested only at the end of the process. Additions to the top of the pile are ongoing as materials become available.

Total MSW Generated by Material, 2018

292.4 million tons

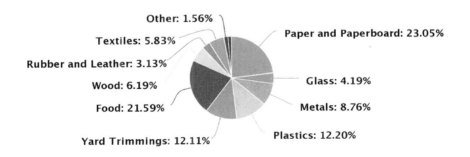

Other: 1.56%
Textiles: 5.83%
Rubber and Leather: 3.13%
Wood: 6.19%
Food: 21.59%
Yard Trimmings: 12.11%
Paper and Paperboard: 23.05%
Glass: 4.19%
Metals: 8.76%
Plastics: 12.20%

STATIC PILE COMPOSTING BACKGROUND

Organic matter forms the most significant part of the total MSW (Municipal Solid Waste) generated. That's because everything we digest is organic, and a lot of what we use is also organic. At the time of this book's publication, the above chart was the most recent data provided by the US Environmental Protection Agency. We can see that food waste and yard trimmings make up more than a third of the total 292.4 million tons of municipal solid waste in the United States. Although paper can be composted, I have excluded it as recycling is more effective than composting paper products.

All organic matter is destined to decompose at some point – it's inevitable. Composting is a natural process that happens regardless of whether we're involved or not. It's nature's way of creating interwoven symbiotic life cycles.

This natural process can greatly benefit us, but it can also be a considerable risk to our wellbeing. When there's an accumulation of tons of organic matter in landfills, the decomposition is often anaerobic (less than 6% oxygen). The buried organic matter produces copious amounts of methane, a highly flammable gas, at this scale. An underground build-up of methane presents an explosion risk, and methane also contributes significantly to damaging the ozone. The anaerobic process is also responsible for forming weak acids that can create potentially toxic leachate. Leachates contaminate streams, lakes, and groundwater reserves at the scales we refer to.

Up until 1976, with the passing of the Resource Conservation and Recovery Act of 1976 (RCRA), municipal solid waste was primarily focussed on hygienically disposing of waste, with landfills being the primary means of doing so. The new legislation stopped the use of open-dumps nationwide. It redefined how municipal solid waste would be managed at a regional level. The focus was moved to tiered priorities of prevention: re-use, recycling, recovery, and as a last resort, disposal.

We now know that methane gas creates significant risks to the earth's ability to host human life. Few people realize how fragile our system is. Our relationship with the sun and the earth's tilt of 23.44 degrees provides us with our seasonal climate changes, which allows for the cyclic life of most animals and plants. Jeopardizing the ozone layer in the stratosphere (15 miles above sea level) causes dangerous ultraviolet light to reach the earth's surface. This has all kinds of negative consequences, including escalating global temperatures.

The Global Warming Potential (GWP) is standardized with carbon dioxide given a score of 1. According to the EPA, methane has a GWP score of 21, indicating its effect over 100 years. The World Watch Institute argues that a score of 72 is more relevant, taken over the next 20 years. They argue that unless methane emissions are radically cut, a domino effect will be initiated that would cause an imbalance in the bio-system that could render the world uninhabitable within two generations. A significant difference between methane and carbon dioxide is their respective dissipation rates. Carbon dioxide takes centuries to dissipate, whereas methane takes decades – hence the argument regarding its impact and allocated score. A more balanced global warming potential score is 38.

AN INTRODUCTION TO STATIC PILE COMPOSTING

Fortunately, the power is in our hands. Suppose we separate organic matter from the rest of our trash and decompose it into compost, even at a residential level. In that case, we could make the difference needed to curb the damages caused to the ozone. The real risk is the depletion of the ozone layer over Antarctica, where the effects of pollution are the greatest. Rising seas are already causing increased groundwater and soil salinity problems in coastal towns.

In the process of composting, we're increasing soil's carbon dioxide absorption ability. Composting is an essential activity for every home, irrespective of the scale at which it is tackled. You're probably wondering, "Dearest Tony, what has all this got to do with static-pile composting?" Well, a lot, actually. Static pile composting is a way of composting that takes minimal effort. It's not as effective (or fast) as hot aerobic composting, which requires more hands-on involvement. But ALL composting is essential for solving the solid waste challenge and increasing the planet's recovery potential. Your garden's improved capacity to sustain life is an incidental added benefit.

I've placed static pile composting in the aerobic composting chapter for a reason. I'm going to show you two ways of managing a static pile. To clarify, static piles are piles of organic material that are rarely turned. These piles are only turned when you harvest your ready compost from the bottom of the pile – usually sometime between six and 12 months.

Static-pile composting can occur in open piles, where organic materials are left to decompose slowly. To effectively compost, you don't need to use a compost bin. Although bins help organize materials, keep pests out of the compost and make it appear cleaner, they aren't necessary for composting.

A holding unit is a simple construction used to keep decomposing materials in order as they decay. It may be easier to compost by using a holding unit. Except for placing the material in the bin as it becomes available, no other labor is required.

In these systems, non-woody materials like grass clippings, vegetable crop trimmings, garden weeds, and leaves can be used. Because the process does not activate thermophilic microorganisms, the process is much slower. By chopping or shredding the materials, mixing greens and browns, and maintaining proper moisture, the processing time can be reduced to just a few months.

While hot composting is generally interrupted by adding fresh material, static-pile decomposition occurs at different levels within the pile. Adding raw material to the top of the pile results in a layered pile with the lower layers increasingly more decomposed. Finished compost is found at the bottom of the pile, while partially decomposed materials can be found near the top. This requires a way for you to remove the finished compost from the lower half once or twice a year.

While you can pile a mix of materials (about two parts of brown to one part of green) in a random heap on the ground as it becomes available, having a way of keeping everything together makes it more accessible. Snow fencing, hardware cloth, old wooden pallets, and stacked cinder blocks are examples of holding units. Bins made of wood, plastic, or metal are commercially available in various sizes and styles. Chapter 9 contains plans for building simple units.

In static pile composting, organic matter is piled up and broken down by bacteria, fungi, and actinomycetes. As the pile decomposes, heat is released, and nutrients are released into the compost. The highest temperature reached determines whether the pile is considered hot or cold. While most static piles fail to activate thermophilic microbes, there are ways to increase temperatures. Composting is spontaneous if there's enough moisture, oxygen, and bioavailable organic matter in the right proportions of carbon and nitrogen. In such a state, the process will always be hot. Cold composting happens when one of those factors is less than ideal.

Just to clarify, the difference between hot and cold composting is:

- **Hot Pile** (*reaches **above** 105 degrees Fahrenheit in the pile's center*). Weed seeds, pathogens, and parasite eggs can survive for several days at temperatures as high as 135 degrees Fahrenheit. At higher temperatures, decomposition is faster. Hot piles require more upkeep than cold piles because interrelated elements need to be monitored and responded to. Proper aeration and moisture levels are required to maintain the microbial activity, regulate the temperature, and distribute heat evenly throughout the pile.

- **Cold Pile** (*maximum temperature **below** 105 degrees Fahrenheit*). The limited access to oxygen, no turning, and continuous adding of fresh materials slows the process. This impacts the microbial activity and the temperatures. Weed seeds and pathogens in the cold composting process remain unaffected and will thus be present in the final compost. This process requires minimum effort, and if added materials are wisely chosen, they can produce quality compost. It is prudent not to add high-risk materials. See the list below.

STATIC PILE COMPOSTING METHODS

The static pile composting process can be passive or dynamic in its in situ state. We ignore what's happening below the surface in the passive process, focused on what we add to the top. In the dynamic static pile process, we force some air through the pile while it remains intact and static. This is also commonly referred to as the forced-air static pile process.

Dynamic Static Pile Composting

Forced aeration involves using a combination of perforated pipes under the composting material and a vacuum or fan blower system to move the air through the compost.

Static-Pile Material Options

Cold composting temperatures are ineffective in neutralizing pathogens and weed seeds. To prevent creating contaminated compost, some materials need to be excluded from the process.
Below is a list of materials suitable for static pile composting.

- **Grass Clippings (17:1)** - Avoid clippings from diseased grass and grass treated with pesticides or herbicides

- **Yard Trimmings (12:1)** - Pruned branches, trimmed vegetables, spent plants, flower buds from your own garden. Avoid plants that have been treated.

- **Leaves (60:1)** - Deciduous leaves are the best option for static composting. Evergreen leaves are higher in decay-resistant lignin, and shredding helps speed the composting process up.

- **Weeds (15:1)** - Weeds compost well but take particular care to ensure that reproductive parts are excluded – rhizomes and seed heads. Remove flowers.

- **Sawdust (400:1)** – Use untreated and unpainted sawdust, and exclude plywood and chipboard sawdust.

- **Food Scraps (15:1)** – Static compost piles are unsuitable for food scraps. A more effective alternative is Trench composting.

- **Wood Chips (500:1)** – Woodchips are high in carbon and should be used sparingly - mainly to control humidity levels.

- **Cardboard and Paper (400:1)** – Recycling paper is better for the environment. Recyclers don't accept soiled paper, so incorporate that into your compost. Wet and shred paper products before adding it to the pile.

Figure 65: Static Pile Materials

NEGATIVE AERATION

In negative aeration, the air is drawn through the composting material from the lower levels of the pile using vacuum suction. I've developed a simple technique for backyard composters that makes this much easier than it sounds. In commercial composting operations, vacuum pumps are used. The process includes a process where the air mass is drawn through biofilters to remove odors. The process I'm suggesting is nothing like that. It's a cost-effective way of getting oxygen to compost-producing microorganisms.

In scaled operations, the criticism of negative (vacuum) aeration include:

- Fine particles and moisture are drawn into the pipelines and blowers, increasing the risk of clogging.

- Compost air may be corrosive, increasing wear-and-tear on the piping and blower.

- If a biofilter is used, it is essential to ensure additional air is added to the exhaust air to reduce the temperature before it is filtered.

The main advantage of negative aeration in commercial operations is improved control of odors if combined with a biofilter. In our backyard operations, this is not one of our primary concerns. We're interested in getting airflow to our microorganisms at the lowest cost and effort possible to optimize our process. Also, our suggested method has none of the above risks as there are no blowers, filters, or pipes that can clog.

Static pile composting has its limitations – mainly controlling humidity and aeration. We can solve the problem by using negative aeration – creating a vacuum at the top and drawing air in through the pile from the bottom. What you need is a relatively airtight environment for your static pile.

My composting bins are made from old wooden pallets covered with a high micron plastic – polytunnel plastic. This limits environmental cooling effects (wind and rain) and the release of odors that could attract pests. As a static pile environment, it gives me more control. Three sides of the bin are static, with the front made of removable slats, allowing me easy access when I need it. The removable front sections are also covered. I've attached wiggle wire strips on the top of the three pallets that form the sides and back, and I've done the same on the inside of the removable top slat.

Before I build my pile, I lay a network of three 2 inch plastic pipes, equally spaced, at the bottom. The pipes are interlinked on one end, and the parallel pipes each have six 3/8 inch holes drilled across their length. The closed-off end is positioned within the pile, and the open end sticks out, unobstructed by debris. Behind the back pallet-side, I've erected a pole with a V-shape at the top that sticks about 18 inches out above the top of the bins. Using a tarp and the wiggle wire, I can securely but loosely attach a lid to the bin when I need to.

In the middle of that tarp (*lid*), I've secured a ring big enough for a rake handle to fit through. I've also created a type of flap valve on the tarp. You can do this by sticking a rather big spacer on the bottom side of the tarp – on the opposite side of the ring attachment. The spacer serves to add rigidity to the outside of the one-directional valve we're creating. The inner dimension of the spacer (or whatever you use) should be about 2 inches. Once the spacer's adhesive is dry, cut a hole in the tarp in the middle of the spacer. Now, attach a flap on the opposite side of the tarp – one that covers the hole amply. The flap can have a spacer too – aligned to the one at the bottom.

You've created a one-way valve that will allow air to be released from the pile while preventing it from returning. Essentially, you're creating a bellow using your compost pile. When the lid, attached on four sides, is lifted, the valve closes and creates a vacuum. Because pipes let air in below your compost pile, the action will suck air through the pile to fill that vacuum. The one-way valve opens when the lid is lowered and allows the air from the pile to escape. Repeating the process will aerate your pile.

Every six weeks, I aerate the static pile this way. I lift the lid using the pivot at the back end and a rake-handle through the ring on the tarp. Leave enough tarp free above the pile so that this action is possible. Aeration must be accompanied by some hydration; otherwise, your pile will become too dry, and the microorganisms will become inactive. Also, aerating a dry batch has fire risks at this level of oxygen supply. Using this technique to create a vacuum that draws the air in from the bottom and through the batch, repeat the action two to three times for ample aeration.

Positive Aeration

In positive aeration, the air is pushed into the pile from the bottom and through the materials to the top. In an open pile, positive aeration provides better airflow distribution. In a contained pile, as described above, negative aeration has a similar oxygen distribution profile as one with air forced in from the bottom with a blower. However, *positive* aeration is more effective at cooling the composting pile overall because of the increased air velocity produced by blowers. It is also less expensive (read cheap) to automate.

In more extensive operations, the fans used are similar to those used for jumping castles. You may choose to use your leaf blower set on its lowest setting in smaller piles. By attaching the blower to a pipe network at the bottom of the pile, you can force air through. To avoid blowing your pile to pieces, you may want to construct a way that only lets some of the air from the blower enter the pile.

Suppose you want to automate your dynamic static pile. In that case, cost-effective humidity and temperature sensor kits are available from STEM shops such as Arduino with their inexpensive *Explore IoT Kit*. The kit's internet connectivity allows you to remotely monitor your pile's status and activate an inline blower when needed. The standard backyard pile is minimally 3 x 3 x 3 feet, i.e., 27 cubic feet. Ideally, you want a blower that produces less than 200 cubic feet per minute (CFM).

A 15-30 cm thick insulated blanket of material (such as mature compost) must be used to cover piles when forced aeration is being used to minimize odors. Negative aeration necessitates the use of a cover. A concrete pad with a ventilated floor and air holes running the length of the pad is an alternative design for forced aeration systems. Positive or negative forced aeration can be achieved by using the ventilated floor. Removing and setting up air pipes is less hassle when emptying the bins. In well-designed flooring systems, leachate can be collected and reused to add moisture to the pile.

Passive Static Pile Composting

Forming a pile of raw material is the first step in the passive composting pile method. Porosity can be restored by using a light auger to stir the batch occasionally. The passive movement of air through the pile is the means of aeration. To allow for this passive air movement, the pile must be medium-sized. Anaerobic zones form if the pile is too large.

The mixing of raw materials should be given special attention. There must be sufficient porosity and structure to ensure adequate aeration during all stages of composting. You don't have to put in a lot of time or effort with the passive composting method. Composting leaves is a typical application of this technique. Anaerobic conditions are more likely to develop because aeration is a passive process. As a result, there is an increased risk of odor issues.

Most static piles are fed gradually from the kitchen and yard, so the decomposition rate will vary. As is true for all compost preparation methods, smaller particles decompose more quickly in compost. It will optimize your composting process if you shred the parts you add. To keep the bottom of the pile partially aerated, use straw, twigs, or even an oak palette as a base. The pallet allows excess moisture to drain and also aids natural aeration.

Keep a bucket of wood shavings or straw handy at the pile. When adding kitchen scraps, cover them with sawdust or straw. Decomposition will be aided, moisture retained, and the smell of the pile will be masked. Turning your compost for this method is unnecessary, but occasionally flipping your pile will help deal with anaerobic pockets and speed up decomposition.

IN-VESSEL AEROBIC COMPOSTING

Composting in bins can be done with or without a lid or with or without a wooden bin. Forced aeration static piles can be found in some bins, and these follow the same rules as forced aeration piles. The material in non-aerated bins must be turned regularly to maintain aerobic composting.

Most composting systems work as batch systems. A blend of carbon-rich material (brown) and nitrogen-rich material (green) combined in alternating layers at a ratio of 30:1. The mixture then goes through the different phases of heating and cooling, turning and wetting, and ensuring enough oxygen until it is stable and fully processed.

Composting small amounts of waste in a rotating tumbler is an additional in-vessel option. The upper portion of the tube is filled with a 30:1 carbon-to-nitrogen ratio mixture of organic materials. The first baffle plate is where the mix will be placed. To aerate the compost, it is rotated after the tube has filled from the first baffle plate to the top, making it possible to add more compost mix to the tube. Composting should be complete when the material at the bottom of the angled tube is dark brown and fully decomposed. What can fit in the tube will be limited to the amount of rotation that can take place when it is loaded.

A continuous system would be a bin of about a cubic yard in size at home. You continuously add fresh material, occasionally wet, and tip once it is full. The tipped compost/fresh material is then covered with a tarp and left to complete the process.

PROS AND CONS OF DIFFERENT AEROBIC COMPOSTING METHODS

Each composting method has its benefits and disadvantages. Let's review the respective advantages and disadvantages of the different aerobic composting processes.

MANAGED AERATION COMPOSTING

Advantages
- An adaptable composting process that yields good results
- Can process more significant amounts of raw materials faster
- It is possible to alter the operation based on material availability
- Aeration is by turning, so the structure and porosity of the mix are less critical
- This process creates a stable compost compared to other methods
- If the pile is turned until temperatures stabilize, no additional curing is required
- The process produces a finer-texture compost due to the repeated turning

Disadvantages:
- Influenced by weather conditions
- Requires hands-on management to its size and available space
- It is the most labor-intensive process, especially during the first couple of weeks
- Turning a pile can take time, depending on the level of assistance available

PASSIVE COMPOSTING PILES

Advantages:
- The least demanding on your time and attention
- Once the pile is formed, you only need to rotate it a few times a year to maintain minimal aeration
- This is the most common choice for home composters for its simplicity and its allowance of adding materials throughout the year

Disadvantages:
- The composting process is prolonged because aeration is passive, and turnings are infrequent
- Up to one year is required for the compost to become fully mature
- Increased chance of anaerobic conditions brought about by compaction and lack of adequate aeration means the potential for odors is more significant
- The piles must be smaller than other methods to promote aeration

- Because the piles generally are built without any protective covering, they are subject to the effects of weather conditions. Cold weather can slow the process, while heavy precipitation can ruin pile porosity and cause runoff and leaching. Excessive drying caused by winds and high ambient temperatures can stop the composting process

AERATED STATIC PILES

Advantages:
- They are more space-efficient
- They can be larger than passive piles because aeration is forced
- It can be done in a single bin
- The increased aeration shortens the time required for composting
- The time or temperature-controlled blowers allow for close process control, which results in more minor temperature variation and a more consistent quality compost
- Elevated temperatures increase pathogen and weed seed neutralization
- The insulating layer on the pile helps achieve higher temperatures and prevent excessive ammonia (nitrogen) losses
- Adequate layering and a 30:1 carbon to nitrogen ratio reduce odors being released

Disadvantages:
- Ensuring even aeration requires practice. Uneven aeration can cause uneven composting and an inconsistent product
- The pipe openings may become blocked, preventing aeration. This is difficult to correct during composting because the pipes are buried at the base of the pile
- Damage to the pipes during final harvesting can be a problem
- Some capital investment is required to purchase the necessary equipment for blowers and pipes. Adding temperature and moisture sensors improves the process but has cost implications
- Forced aeration can interrupt moisture retention as it accelerates evaporation and, if excessive, will prevent compost stabilization
- Because there is no turning involved, managing moisture content is more difficult

IN-VESSEL SYSTEMS

Advantages:
- A reduced vulnerability to the effects of the weather
- Better odor control

- Greater control of the quality and consistency of the product (compared to static piles)
- Space-efficient as no additional space is required for turning
- Can process more depending on the vessel or structure
- Requires less labor than piles because turning is an integrated feature
- Vessels can absorb and trap ambient heat, accelerating the process

Disadvantages:
- More expensive than passive piles
- Quality of vessel is essential. Many commercially available products are ineffective
- Excessive turning can prevent adequate temperatures from developing, impeding the pathogen and weed seed killing processes
- Bins filled too high can result in compaction and inadequate aeration
- These systems have less flexibility than other systems, particularly concerning access to material in the decomposition phases

IN SUMMARY

So far, we have learned that by feeding your soil, your garden can contain all the minerals needed to grow healthy and high-yield crops. Bacteria hold the highest amount of nitrogen in their bodies and many other essential nutrients that your plants require. Without the population of a thriving microorganism in your soil, these nutrients will remain unavailable to your plants.

The soil food web contains tiers of predator-prey-related microorganisms. These organisms release the nitrogen captured in their bodies into the soil by consuming each other. This nitrogen, and other minerals, then become available to plants. Organic material is everything that was once living but has died. The plants need the nutrients in the organic matter but cannot break it down into a simplified form that they can absorb. The function of bacteria, fungi, and actinomycetes in your soil produces the enzymes needed to break the organic matter down, absorbing it into their bodies – still unavailable to plants.

Enter the second-tier consumers – the nematode, protozoa, microarthropods, and macroarthropods. By consuming the bacteria, fungi, and actinomycetes, these organisms make the simplified nutrients and compounds available to plants through bodily functions or in their demise – maybe at the *hand* of a predatory nematode.

Your plants release exudates through their surface and roots. The first-tier organisms (bacteria, fungi, actinomycetes) are attracted to these exudates that contain amino acids, sugars, and minerals. This attraction of the first-tier organisms has a chain reaction – the attraction of predators that feed on them. This is a perfect example of symbiosis. The plants provide the soil food web with what it needs. The soil food web reciprocates by releasing what the plant needs through a chain of predator-prey activities.

Because the feeding source originates at the plants' roots (food for the first-tier organisms), the release of hormones, growth regulators, antibiotics, minerals, and enzymes all takes place at the roots – where it is needed. This makes pesticides counter-productive as they destroy the soil food web, the very source of our plants' feeding and inoculation processes.

Compost production, especially aerobic composting, is essentially microorganism farming. The thermal cycles of aerobic composting have the added advantage of sterilizing your organic matter and killing weed seeds and pathogens. This natural process requires your intervention to ensure sufficient airflow and moisture and the right balance between carbon matter and nitrogen-rich materials.

Aside from the fact that organic matter is a primary source of nutrients for plants, it also has a significant impact on the physical properties of soil, including water-holding capacity and the ability to exchange nutrients and buffer them. These properties are critical in regulating the uptake of nutrients by plants and retaining them in the soil. Small amounts of certain organic substances (such as highly dispersed humic acids) have also been shown to positively impact plant growth and development.

The essentials are a carbon-to-nitrogen ratio of approximately 30:1 while considering bioavailability. Too much nitrogen and you will get a whiff of ammonia; too much carbon and the process will slow or stop. Also, suppose the undecomposed carbon is added to your soil (in the absence of nitrogen). In that case, the organisms will grab onto the nitrogen in the soil they're added to, depriving the plants. More than 60% moisture, and you'll obstruct oxygen supply that will, by definition, result in anaerobic conditions.

Curing is a process that ensures all the carbon that can be consumed is now part of living or dead microorganisms. What remains is rich humus, the color of 70% dark chocolate – not black and not caramel-colored. This is often referred to as *black gold*. This is the substance that holds untold benefits to the health of your soil. In the next chapter, we review some anaerobic composting processes. Chapter 8 shows you how to use this compost to make compost tea. Compost tea further extends the benefits of compost, making foliage application possible – an effective pesticide.

7. ANAEROBIC COMPOSTING

BACKGROUND

The anaerobic digestion (AD) process occurs when microorganisms break down organic matter *in the absence of oxygen*. Clay tablets found in the Mesopotamian Valley some 4,300 years ago refer to composting. For the past 240 years, anaerobic digestion has primarily been for methane production as a renewable energy source. As much as 150 years ago, the street lamps in Exeter, United Kingdom, were fueled by AD-produced methane gas. Typically, anaerobic digestion for biogas production occurs in a sealed vessel called a reactor.

Reactors come in various sizes and designs specific to the site and feedstock conditions. Typically, feedstock with total solids above 30% is uneconomical, though high-solid digestion technologies improve. The complexity of the microbial communities needed to digest the waste is the main challenge. The process goes through three phases, each requiring different microorganisms to convert organic waste into methane-rich biogas and a stabilized digestate. Balancing the populations of these microorganisms is one of the operational challenges of AD.

Typically, AD reactors are fed with high volumes of waste from food processing plants, high-moisture manure from beef feedlots and swine farms, and used cooking oil from restaurants. High energy crops (like maize) are grown for AD processes. Anaerobic composting can process food waste and almost all organic materials, including fats, oils, and greases. The process is ineffective in breaking down products with high cellulose or lignin content (wood, for instance). Each organic material has individual chemical and physical properties that impact the digestibility of the material.

Anaerobic digestion produces biogas composed of methane (CH_4), hydrogen sulfide (H_2S), carbon dioxide (CO_2), and water vapor. One of the applications for the residue of the process is producing a peat moss substitute. This residue is called digestate and consists of undigested inert material and water. Lignin-rich materials form a significant portion of the digestate used to manufacture stall staw for animals to sleep on.

Anaerobic digestion goes through a series of decomposition and transformation processes. The freshly added organic matter is first broken down through an enzymatic process of hydrolysis. Complex polymers (carbohydrates and proteins) are reduced to soluble monomers (sugars and amino acids) in this process. The second set of microorganisms creates an acidogenic digestate, converting the monomers to short-chain organic acids, alcohols, hydrogen, ammonia, and carbon dioxide.

Acidogenesis (the second phase) occurs early in the process. Hence, the buried organic matter at this stage is a highly hygroscopic substrate (moisture attractor and retainer). It is also rich in minerals, mainly phosphorus and nitrogen-loaded microorganisms' remnants. If you added any fibrous material like leaves and wood, that would only be partly decomposed at this stage.

In the last stage of the anaerobic digestion process, the methanogenic phase, we're introduced to a new actor in the decomposition process – archaea. Originally thought to belong to the bacteria family, archaea share properties with Eukaryota (fungi) too. They are unique in their methanogenesis ability – methane production from acetates and hydrogen.

The methanogenic microbes are sensitive to altering pH and prefer a pH between 5.0 and 8.5, depending on the species. At this stage, part of your buried organic matter has been broken down into a sludge high in nutrients such as potassium (K) and ammonium ($NH4+$). A high levels of ammonium is toxic to plants, but it is beneficial at lower doses. For this reason, it's inadvisable to plant directly on your buried food scraps for at least a year. Weather conditions also play a role – the risk of ammonium toxicity is higher in warmer temperatures.

Comparative nitrogen availability for anaerobic composting is significantly higher than nitrogen available from aerobic composting. The combination of both aerobic and anaerobic compost creates a perfect world for your plants. Add to that some leguminous green compost as cover plants and your crop will outperform any crop treated with synthetic fertilizer – with the added benefit of better water retention, pest and disease resilience, and pH buffering. I would want to live in your garden if I was a plant.

AMMONIUM TOXICITY

When excess nitrogen is available, plants store the surplus. Nitrate can effectively be stored by plants, but too much ammonium can cause cell damage. Excessive ammonium storage causes ammonium toxicity. In tomato plants, this can be seen by the leaf-tips turning brown. In aerobic composting, nitrifying bacteria converts the ammonium to nitrate, which poses no risk to the plants.

Soil below 60 degrees Fahrenheit suppresses nitrifying organisms' functionality, as do low oxygen levels and low pH (acidity). Therefore, it becomes evident that adding traditional compost to the later stages of anaerobic composting will significantly benefit the health of your soil. Ensure that the added compost is stable; otherwise, it will leach the nitrogen from the anaerobic mix.

TRENCH COMPOSTING

Trench composting is the easiest way to reduce waste being sent to landfills and benefit your garden's soil in the process. In essence, in trench composting we bury household scraps in the garden and allow nature to do the rest. There are some considerations, though, and understanding the process will help you balance your garden's needs with the waste disposal element.

First, we note that this is an anaerobic (sans oxygen) process performed by a range of microorganisms quite different from our aerobic consumers. A key difference is the absence of the thermophilic microorganisms responsible for creating temperatures above 105 degrees Fahrenheit. The temperatures reached in anaerobic composting will not kill pathogens and weed seeds, so don't add seed heads or anything that may be contaminated. Also, anaerobic microorganisms are primarily bacterial and

archaean, so the lignin-efficient fungi in aerobic composting are poorly represented. In the absence of fungi, burying wood and leaves is not advised – they will take years to decompose. This narrows your choice to softer, high-moisture organic products like food waste, fresh-mowed lawn clippings, and the like.

Organic material buried in a trench can take as long as a year to stimulate a healthy soil food web. The diversity of microorganisms is what makes your soil more productive. Organic waste is the plant's food and vice versa; the plant's carbon, released via its roots, is what the microorganisms thrive on.

Different composting techniques stimulate the proliferation of diverse microorganisms. Leaf mold, for instance, promotes the growth of fungi. In contrast, hot composting encourages thermophilic organisms (and a whole range of others). Trench composting is a cold, anaerobic process performed by microorganisms that thrive without oxygen (or less than 6% oxygen).

With time, their presence attracts other local microorganisms to join the process. But there's a way to speed this up.

MAKING SLOW TRENCH COMPOSTING FASTER

There is a way to influence the available microorganisms to get the job done faster. By pre-fermenting the food scraps and organic kitchen waste, we inoculate the leftovers with effective microorganisms (EM®). These microbes are carefully selected to create a tipping point for other microorganisms to perform better, reducing the decomposition time from 52 weeks (a year) to two weeks.

EM is used in Bokashi composting, but alternative combinations of lactic acid bacteria and yeast spores have a similar effect. If, for instance, you add fungi mycelium (fungi root), your trench compost process will accelerate significantly.

HOW DOES TRENCH COMPOSTING WORK?

Trench composting is one of the older forms of composting. Early on, it was recognized that decomposing organic matter was a health risk, so it was buried in a pit. The plants around the holes where organic material was buried flourished, leading to the process being purposefully applied to agricultural endeavors.

First Variation – The Pit

The first form of strategic composting was the pit method, the lazy man's alternative to trench composting – an abbreviated version. It remains a viable option in areas where you want to enrich the soil where tree roots restrict digging a trench, and digging a pit under the tree's drip zone is the best option.

The pros are that it's straightforward and requires no turning or need for carbon-rich browns (though adding some leaves will add value). The cons are that you need to dig a new hole about a foot deep for every addition. This would be impractical in winter (unless pre-dug in summer).

The Pit Evolved – The Trench

The trench is an expanded strategic solution to the pit. It offers the advantage of allowing food scraps to be added daily. After adding the food scraps to the 1- to 2-foot-deep trench, cover it to prevent rodents and other pests from accessing it.

Buried waste can take a while to decompose in trench composting. While some writers advise planting directly on the recently filled trench, I have found that this causes root rot and other pathogenic diseases. Remember, the only active microorganisms are those on the food and the microbes already in the soil.

HOW LONG DOES TRENCH COMPOSTING TAKE?

Unless the food scraps were inoculated with external microorganisms, like fermenters in Bokashi, it takes a while for microorganism activity to break the food down. In highly anaerobic soil, like clay, buried food can take years to break down.

Suppose your soil is classified as loam (a balance of sand and silt and a lesser portion of clay). In that case, your buried food waste will stimulate local microorganisms' activity. With increased microorganism activity, your food scraps could be decomposed in six to seven months.

My advice is that you commit to an annual rotational plan:

Year 1 - September to February:
Prepare an 18- to 24-inch-deep trench in late summer and fill it with food scraps throughout fall and winter. Cover it with soil as you go – both on top and the sides. Coverage should be about 8 inches to prevent scavengers from unearthing the treasure.

Year 1 – March to August :
Your first trench should be filled and covered – it will serve as a pathway throughout the warmer months. This gives the ammonium a chance to dissipate into nitrite. Dig a new trench adjacent to the buried scraps (give about a 6-inch gap) and fill that over the summer months. Don't plant on the trench made in winter yet. It is good to wet the trench before adding food scraps as it aids the initial hydrolization process.

Prepare a third trench adjacent to the current food scraps trench before the winter freeze sets in. Again, allow a gap of about 6 inches between the trenches.

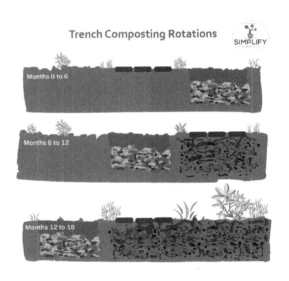

Trench Composting Rotations

Year 2 – September to February:
In the trench you filled with organic matter last winter, you now have soil that's abundantly rich in natural nitrogen. The top 8 inches have some microbial activity – just the usual local residents. Consider adding traditional compost to boost that microbial activity and add some organic matter (humus).

This is not a requirement, but the benefits are significant. The organisms in anaerobic composting effectively preserve nitrogen but do little else. On the other hand, the traditional compost microorganisms are great at nitrifying any ammonium residue, improving soil tilth, fixing pH, promoting aggregate formation, and improving soil moisture management.

LENGTH OF TRENCH
A friend once told me that there's a German expression that translates as, "A horse never jumps higher than it has to." The meaning I took from that is, "Do what is needed, and no more."

I dig my trenches a yard or two long at a time. That way, I limit the damage I may cause to an established soil food web. Removing the soil from the trench disrupts the ecosystem that I need for breaking the food scraps down to compost.

Suppose I limit the time of that disruption. In that case, I can use the residential microorganisms to complement the ones already involved in causing the food scraps to decay. I don't want the food to rot, so I use the leftovers to feed beneficial microorganisms, which enrich our soil.

I realize it's called composting (as it relates to decomposition), but you're actually farming with microorganisms. Compost is a visible byproduct of microorganism farming. It is host to billions of beneficial microbes essential to soil wellbeing and healthy, productive plants.

These microorganisms are also responsible for plant resilience to disease and even pests.

WHAT CAN YOU ADD TO TRENCH COMPOSTING?

Trench composting is a product of the ancient practice of using pits to dump organic matter that could rot and attract rats and flies and cause diseases. These pits were often burial grounds for animals that died of diseases and were thus unsuitable for human consumption and other organic waste.

Often, the process included both incineration and burial. The pits were also used to dispose of litter, though our ancient forefathers were less messy in some ways—their primary portion of trash was ash and food scraps. Resources were scarce, so hides, horns, and hooves were used for shelter, tools, and other purposes.

I make this point because trench composting is an effective way to use all food scraps to benefit the soil. That said, here are some exclusions:

If you're burying bones, two feet deep is the minimum to hide the smell from scavenger animals. I bury them in a hole even deeper than two feet.

Exclude yard plants that seem diseased. A good motto is: if in doubt, leave it out.

Exclude anything that has been treated with insecticide. Added food waste should not have been treated with an antibacterial spray or solvent.

Do not add weeds that have gone to seed. Why make trouble for yourself? Weeds are defined as plants that spend most of their energy reproducing. Their contribution to soil carbon is only 20%, compared to trees that contribute 80% and vegetables that contribute 60%. The microorganisms need carbon.

Exclude pet waste that may contain diseases.

Exclude cut flowers that come from a florist. These are usually treated with a fungicide that will kill the fungi, an essential component of your decomposition process.

HOW DO YOU BUILD A COMPOST TRENCH?

The Trench
The average spade is 6 to 8 inches wide and 9 to 11 inches long. You need a trench about 18 inches deep and 12 inches wide – nearly twice as deep as your spade blade length and a bit wider than a spade.

Use a space that does not have a lot of foot traffic but is also close enough to monitor any rodent or raccoon activity. Rats and other scavengers won't be a problem if you bury your food scraps sufficiently deep to avoid the smell attracting them.

Vegetable Garden Trench Composting
If you use your established vegetable garden, the area surrounding the food-scrap-filled trench will show benefits within the first year. This happens as the local microorganisms get activated by the increased food availability.

Trench Composting Around Shrubs
Your scrubs can also benefit from trench composting. Test the soil around the scrub to establish where the root system is at its extremity. Dig a trench around the shrub about a foot from the end of the root system, avoiding damaging the roots.

With shrubs, I would dig the trench all the way around the scrub to allow water accumulation and the recovery of any damaged roots. Make sure to water the channel before adding the scraps. This promotes the mobility of surrounding microorganisms and speeds up the decomposition process.

Trench Composting Around Trees

When using trench composting around trees, take care not to damage the root system. Generally, I prefer to make a selection of pits around the tree. Here I also water the holes regularly before adding any scraps to the pit.

Pits can be dug using an auger, but you need to be sure that you're at least at the tree's dripline. The dripline is on the verge of the tree's rain shadow, where rain that is caught by the leaves primarily lands.

If it is safe to do so, dig all the pits beforehand. If, however, you have pets or children who could hurt themselves running in the area of the holes, delay making them until they're needed or cordon the area off.

HOW DEEP DO YOU BURY COMPOST?

Depending on the content of what you are adding to the trench, depths can be between a foot deep to as much as 30 inches.

BOKASHI TRENCH COMPOSTING

If you add fermented kitchen scraps to your trench, a product of EM® and Bokashi, then trench composting requires a different approach. Here are the main differences:

- Bokashi composting doesn't attract pests as the smell is unappealing to them. This means that you can get away with only burying your fermented scraps in a **12-inch deep** trench.

- You mix the fermented mass with some soil before burying it.

- The most significant difference is that you can plant on the trench after two weeks due to limited ammonium production.

- Remember to mix a portion of the backfill soil with the Bokashi fermented food waste *AND* then cover that mix with unmixed dirt to limit rodent curiosity even further.

- As described above, adding traditional compost has further benefits for your soil's health.

KITCHEN SCRAPS WITHOUT MEAT, FAT, OR BONES IN TRENCH COMPOSTING

Suppose your kitchen separates the scraps that go to the holding bin to exclude meat-related products. In that case, you can also get away with having a **12-inch deep** trench – 4 inches of scraps and 8 inches of backfill soil previously removed.

Remember to add water to the trench before adding the waste to speed the process up. After adding the backfill dirt, some compaction will help limit oxygen getting to the process.

Suppose your kitchen scraps include meat, small bones, fat, or other meat-related products. In that case, you will need to bury your organic material at least **18-inches deep** – with 12-inches of backfill dirt on top of the kitchen scraps.

If you regularly dispose of larger bones (for instance, from roasts), you will need to dig a **24-inch trench**. Adding leaf mold will accelerate the decomposition process. Leaf mold has a dense fungi population that decomposes more rigid materials like cellulose, lignin, and bones.

With any meat-related scraps, it's important not to mess any fat, gravies, or juices on the soil used to cover the organic matter. The whole idea of burying it 24 inches deep is to hide any trace from rodents, raccoons, or even bears. Their survival depends on their olfactory glands (sense of smell), so they only need a hint to uncover your buried treasure.

DOES TRENCH COMPOSTING ATTRACT RATS?

If you follow my advice above, you ought not to have any problems with rodents, stray cats, or other scavengers. The essential factor is to reduce air to and from the buried scraps.

Allowing air to reach the organic matter will kill the anaerobic microorganisms. Allowing air from the trench will carry the smell of your scraps

Just a reminder – both depth and side cover is essential. Make sure that you bury the food and cover the side of the food sufficiently. What I do is accumulate waste in an airtight container in my fridge. Once the container is complete – about a gallon – I add it to my trench to maximize the continuation of organic material.

TRENCH COMPOSTING ADVANTAGES

The greatest attraction of trench composting is the ability to incorporate waste into your soil – with almost no hassle. It's an easy process and a perfect solution for gardeners with small spaces who want to boost their nitrogen levels (and who doesn't).

Traditional composting requires a mix of brown and green material – trench composting does not. Even static piles need space – trench composting is a case of bury and forget.

Trench composting generally reaches deeper than other forms of composting. This helps improve soil from the bottom up.

Personally, I think there are two disadvantages – probably a reflection on my personality rather than on the process. Firstly, the process is lengthy. I'm not the best at delayed gratitude for gardening, so I use the Bokashi fermentation to speed the process up. The Bokashi fermentation reduces the composting time 26 times from 52 weeks to a mere two weeks.

Secondly, it requires digging trenches. I don't mind digging in wetter seasons, but in winter, it's horrid.

TRENCH COMPOSTING IN WINTER

While digging trenches in the winter is a form of torture, suppose you dig your trenches in warmer weather and bury your scraps over winter. In that case, the process will not be negatively affected, and it will merely freeze until warmer weather.

TRENCH COMPOSTING SUMMARY

Trench composting provides a benefit that other composting methods seldom achieve – an effective solution to compaction. Trench composting occurs at depths not generally reached through other composting methods – at depths where mature plant roots reach. This means that at the height of a plant's fruit production phase it has access to fresh nutrients.

It is also a very effective way of eliminating food waste that you generally would not add to a compost bin – like meats, fish, and fats. Requiring limited space, trench composting definitely has a place in a gardener's composting regime. Trench composting is an easy and effective way to replenish the soil's vitality using food scraps. When combined with fermenting processes, like Bokashi, trench composting offers maximum returns for minimum effort. Adding traditional compost even further boosts your soil's health. The message is clear—whatever you do, compost.

LEAF MOLD COMPOSTING

There are many ways to manage leaves in fall. You could mulch them with a mulching mower, collect them with a mower, blow or rake them into heaps, or use a vac-blower to shred, collect, and store them for later use. Whatever way you choose, they're a fabulous resource.

Leaves are the tree's primary energy converters and heat regulators. Perennial trees shed their leaves annually. Shed leaves consist mainly of cellulose and lignin, and leaves with high lignin levels are slow to decompose.

Because leaves are high in cellulose and lignin, they are resistant to bacteria breakdown. Fungi do initial decomposition with bacteria taking over later in the process. This section reviews how straightforward it is to improve your soil with leaves that are often discarded without a second thought.

LEAF COMPOSTING OR LEAF MOLD?

Leaf mold is the *fungal* decomposition of leaves in a mainly anaerobic environment. On the other hand, leaf composting is a hybrid form of leaf mold manufacturing. The difference between leaf mold and leaf composting is the addition of some nitrogen, which causes the pile to heat up, indicating some thermophilic *bacterial* activity. In general, fungi become inactive at higher temperatures but resume their activities when the temperature drops again.

Leaf composting is the process of creating an environment where microorganisms can flourish with the objective of reconstituting leaves into soil-benefitting leaf mold. The leaves that fall to the ground have little composting value in their initial state. They are low in carbon matter, high in decomposition-resistant materials, and tend to either mat or blow away if used as mulch.

However, by adding a little magic in the form of nitrogen, uric acid, carbon, water, and oxygen, you have a prized soil enhancer. To make the magic quicker, try to prevent too much heat from escaping. You can do this by making your piles higher and protecting the pile from wind and rain. Leaf mold, even the hybrid version, doesn't get as hot as bacteria-driven aerobic decomposition processes.

While it is common to refer to the process as composting, the product is actually leaf mold. This is because fungi, and not bacteria, mainly do the breakdown. It is probably the easiest way for a gardener to add value to their soil. Our fungi friends are saprophytes – microorganisms that live off dead or dying organic materials. If they have food and water, they flourish. They need oxygen and hydrogen too, which they are equipped to extract from the water.

HOW DO YOU MAKE LEAF COMPOST
Like with all composting processes, there are five essential ingredients:

- **Carbon** for the microorganisms

- **Nitrogen** for the microorganisms

- **Uric acid** for the fungi. Interesting fact: uric acid causes gout and can be found at high levels in beer. Second to baker's yeast, mushrooms are high in uric acid too. Uric acid is also rich in nitrogen

- **Water** to increase the mobility of microorganisms and act as an energy supply line. Water also helps regulate temperatures and provides fungi with oxygen and hydrogen

- **Oxygen** to help with the oxidation process of the carbon-releasing CO2

- **Heat** speeds up the process. Much of the heat is self-generated, and our role is merely to help prevent that generated heat from escaping. A study done by MIT showed a direct correlation between ambient temperature and decomposition rates

Have you ever seen a fantasy ice castle – like the ones they put up on ice rinks? They're able to do that by minimizing the exposed area of the ice. If you took a BIG block of ice and waited for it to melt, it would take ages. If you took that same massive block of ice and broke it down into tiny pieces, the melting process will be accelerated. The ice block's surface area has increased and is now exposed. More exposure, more surface area exposed to ambient temperature, so faster melting.

The same applies to composting – the more surface area exposed, the more area upon which microorganisms can act, the faster the decomposition. Because the construction of leaves has evolved to balance weight and efficient light exposure, leaves are generally flat. Their flat shape creates a mat of leaves which stick to each other when wet. The flat structure also makes flight possible in windy conditions – similar to a butterfly wing.

It's, therefore, a good idea to shred the leaves before adding them to your compost pile. I shred my leaves four times before they are fine enough. You can use various methods to shred leaves, but here are three suggestions.

- Run over them with a lawnmower that has a catch-bag – you might need to repeat the process a couple of times. You will see how fast 10 bags of leaves can be reduced in volume to fit into a single bag.

- Vacuum them up with blower-vac. A couple of years ago, while using this method, the static caused by the dry leaves created a conduit for a spark between the motor and my bare arm, and it wasn't fun. Lesson learned: Always wear appropriate protective gear.

- Put them through a shredder. Personally, I think it's worth the investment.

YOU'LL NEED THE FOLLOWING TO CREATE LEAF MOLD:

- Lots and lots of **shredded leaves** – enough to create a pile of no less than a 3 foot cube. This is about 40 garbage bags of leaves

- Some* moist **soil taken from a wooded area**

- Some* **horse manure** – good but not essential

- Some **urine** mixed with water – urine is abundant in uric acid, a rich form of nitrogen. Ideally, you'll make a 4 gallon mix, which I will explain below

- **A bin** that can hold a cubic yard of leaves. Take a look at my video on making leaf mold and see what I did. https://youtube.com/watch?v=wUOcIR3RvuM. Alternatively, use a 1 ton bulk bag. They're great for collecting leaves and as a holding unit for leaf mold/compost production

- A couple of sheets of wet newspaper

*The *some* referred to above is about a heaped spade full – or half a 4 gallon plastic shopping bag

MAKING A NITROGEN-RICH WETTING AGENT

To make a wetting agent loaded with nitrogen and microorganisms, you will need:

- A cotton bag or a commercial horticultural compost tea bag

- 5 cups of horse manure

- 5 cups of nutrient-rich soil from a wooded area

- A 2 gallon bucket filled with water and topped up with 2 cups of urine

Place the horse manure and soil in the compost tea bag and soak in the water/urine mix for 48 hours. If you have an air pump (like those used in fish tanks), pumping air into the mixture will speed up the diffusion and proliferation of microorganisms in the solution.

The end product is a nitrogen- and microorganism-rich water solution that radically speeds up decomposition.

MAKING LEAF MOLD PRACTICAL

1. Start with a 6 inch layer of shredded leaves.

2. Drizzle the layer with the urine mixture – wetting enough that a single drop can be squeezed out when squeezed. Please remember that the shredded leaves are electrostatically charged and hydrophobic, repelling water. This means even though spraying the pile may seem to wet it, the layers beneath will still be dry. You will need to ensure all the layers are wet by agitating the pile, stilling in the moisture. Make sure the WHOLE batch is moist.

3. Spread a thin layer of horse manure/soil mixture.

4. Cover with a wet sheet of newspaper.

5. Repeat the previous steps until all the shredded leaves are used up.

6. End with a layer of shredded damp leaves. Use a board or rake to compress the pile. If you have an old rug, covering your pile will help it retain heat and speed up the composting process considerably. It could even reduce the time down to six months! That is 25% of what it usually would take (24 months).

WHAT LEAVES ARE BEST FOR COMPOSTING?
Leaves with a low lignin content are ideal for making leaf compost. Plant matter such as needles, which contain a lot of lignin (a vital building block), has a narrower decay rate than leafier plants, which have less lignin and more nutrients that attract microbes. Lignin protects organic compounds from degradation by acting as a shield.

Lignon-reduced leaves (with higher calcium and nitrogen levels) include ash, cherry, elm, linden, and maple. In six months, these leaves will be completely decomposed.

Beech, birch, oak, hornbeam, and sweet chestnut are examples of unsuitable leaves because they are high in lignin and low in nitrogen. Magnolia and holly are two more plants that should be included in this list. A typical two-year breakdown period is required. Trees like oaks, beech, and sycamore with thick leaves that stick around for a long time have high lignin levels and might leach nitrogen out the soil before giving any back.

HOW LONG DOES IT TAKE FOR LEAVES TO COMPOST?
Leaves vary in their decomposition times. The Long-term Intersite Decomposition Experiment Team (LIDET) study collected leaf litter from 27 North and Central American locations, from the Alaskan tundra to Panamanian rainforests. The research showed that leaves in warm and wet regions decomposed faster than those in cold and dry areas. Leaf-type was also a determinant, with needles (high-lignin) deteriorating much slower than leaves with low levels of lignin.

In nature, leaves take about two years to decompose. As discussed above, decomposition can be reduced to six months in controlled environments.

DO LEAVES COMPOST QUICKER IF SHREDDED?
Leaves are decomposed by the activities of microorganisms – mainly fungi. Because these organisms are tiny, and their action is on the material's surface, maximizing the surface area maximizes their activity.

Consider a loaf of bread. The loaf has six surface areas – two ends, a top and a bottom, and two sides. Cutting six slices increases the surface areas by 6 x 6 = 36 surface areas. The unsliced loaf will take a while to dry out (or grow mold), but the slices will dry out much faster. Repeating the cutting process will increase the exposed surfaces exponentially.

Similarly, shredding your leaves increases the exposed surface area, thus increasing the fungi's activity on the leaves. Shredding and wetting your leaves can halve or even quarter the time required to make leaf mold – and it improves the quality of the end product.

Another handy way to speed up leaf composting is to create a wetting agent made from beer. By mixing a medium bottle of beer, a can of sugar-containing soda, and half a cup of ammonia with two gallons of water, you have an effective composting kick-starter.

WHAT LEAVES SHOULD NOT BE COMPOSTED?

The general rule of thumb, in a non-scientific approach, is to stick to composting thinner leaves. The following is a list of trees and shrubs that have thicker leaves and are higher in lignin content:

- Birch
- Oak
- Hornbeam
- Sweet Chestnut
- Magnolia
- Holly
- Sycamore
- Eucalyptus
- Beech (to a lesser extent)
- Black Walnut

These leaves have high lignin content and might leach nitrogen out of your soil before giving any back when added. For interest's sake: lignin in wood is extracted to make polymers for paints and adhesives—nasty stuff for your garden, good alternative to petroleum. The fungi reduce lignin to a high-humectant substrate.

While lignin is strongly associated with retarded leaf decomposition rates, the leaves' C:N ratio has also been researched and may hold a more vital link to their slow decomposition. Either way, thicker leaves, even in accelerated environments, decompose slower.

IS IT LEGAL TO COLLECT LEAVES TO COMPOST?

Generally speaking, you can collect as much as you want from the gift shops in U.S.A. parks. Otherwise, everything else is strictly forbidden. If you're going to collect leaves from national parks, don't. If you want to find out more, visit

the int.org website and review Principle 4: Leave What You Find - Leave No Trace Center – leave the leaves.

From local municipal parks, first, check with the park's manager. Some counties encourage composters to collect the leaves from parks; others do not. It is essential that you check with your local council – breaking the rules can be expensive.

However, there are no prohibitions on collecting leaves in your own (and friends') gardens. Your leaves, your choice.

WHAT EQUIPMENT DO I NEED TO MAKE LEAF COMPOST?
Leaf Shredder
Some ways of shredding leaves include gathering them in low piles, going over them with a mower, or vacuuming them up with a blower/vac shredder. Alternatively, you can get a leaf shredder. The benefit of a leaf shredder is that it will reduce effort and the volume of leaves. An electric shredder allows you to produce one bag of shredded leaves from several bags of leaves.

An advantage is that shredded leaves compost so much faster. I shred my leaves fine, and an electric shredder allows you to choose between coarse, medium, and fine shredding. Since most electric shredders come with a stand, you can fit a catchment bag to collect the shredded leaves.

You can also use the same shredder to shred paper, a handy additive to the composting processes.

Tarps
A tarp is a handy gardener's tool. You can use it to gather leaves rapidly, cover your compost pile to retain heat, and much more.

1 Ton Bulk Bag
A 1 ton bulk bag is another excellent investment I found really helpful in cultivating leaf mold. The ideal size is 35 inches square and 43 inches deep, and they are airtight and will prevent the compost from losing heat. Woven polypropylene bags are also handy for collecting leaves.

Leaf Scoops

I use scoops that fit on my hands, basically converting them into big plastic shovels. Once you've raked your leaves into piles, use these to scoop the leaves into one of your 1 ton bags – ready for shredding.

Rake

It is easier to rake damp leaves than dry leaves, and it is much easier if you have a light, 30 inch broad leaf rake to use. Rake in the direction of the wind to make it easier. Create multiple piles that you can gather with your hand scoops.

Watering Can

While I usually use a hose to wet my compost heaps, for my leaf compost/mold, I use one of the above wetting regimes. To spread the compost tea evenly, I like using a watering can.

Compost Tea Bags

A compost tea bag allows you to create compost tea without clogging your watering can's sprinkler. The instructions for how to do this are shared above.

WHAT CAN I USE LEAF COMPOST FOR?

Leaf mold is a gold mine for gardeners. It has a high mineral content and can grow plants naturally without additional fertilizer. Contrary to popular belief, leaf mold is beneficial to your lawn. Leaves are the product of the tree roots extracting minerals deep underground and transporting them to the leaves, loading them with many valuable trace minerals.

Leaf mold is one of the best soil conditioners you'll ever use, despite the negative connotations associated with the word "mold." A single leaf mold spore can hold five times its weight in water, and that's on par with peat moss, if not better. Because of this, leaf mold is an excellent mulch to use around the garden. Soil structure and texture are greatly improved when organic matter is added to sandy or clay soils.

Microbes and other beneficial organisms, such as earthworms, thrive in leaf mold environments. As a result, your garden's soil will be vibrant and alive. There's also the fact that it's free! Don't let the lack of leaves in your yard stop you from participating. People are always willing to let you pick up bags of their leaves or let you rake some for them. Find out by talking to your friends and family! If you don't like cleaning up after the leaves in the fall, make friends with them.

It can be used as a mulch, a soil amendment, in containers and raised beds in place of peat moss, and in your compost bin as brown matter.

I turn leaf mold into the soil to a spade depth (about 8 to 11 inches) as a soil amendment. I use between 2 and 3 inches of mulch around plants, careful not to mulch up to the plant's stem or base. Because leaf mold is so hygroscopic, the continuous moisture on the stem can provide an opportunity for diseases.

FAQ
Leaf Composting and Leaf Mold – what's the difference?
Composting is organic matter's controlled aerobic biological decomposition into a stable, humus-like compost product. Molds are different in that the decomposition breakdown is primarily done by fungi – though bacteria are involved to a lesser degree.

Is Leaf Mold a good ground cover?
Leaf mold is highly hygroscopic (attracts and retains water). As a soil additive, this is a great benefit. As a ground cover, this may hinder roots accessing the moisture. That's the long answer. This short answer is that leaf mold is better in the soil than on the ground.

Can I use Leaf Mold as potting soil?
Absolutely! Leaf mold is an excellent option for potting soil. It is rich in nutrients, active with microorganisms, and retains moisture excellently.

BOKASHI COMPOSTING

Almost 40 years ago, decades before soil microorganisms became popular, a Japanese scientist, Professor Teruo Higa, produced a mix he patented and called EM® – for effective microorganisms. These particular organisms have a low impact on humans. But what are they? EM consume toxins from the environment, pathogens from humans, and plant pathogens without harming humans.

The active ingredients of Bokashi, a Japanese term for fermented organic matter, are lactic acid bacteria (LAB), yeast, and phototrophic bacteria. LAB and yeast are also the key ingredients of kombucha, known to improve the gut biome.

The third ingredient, phototrophic bacteria, harnesses solar energy for growth and metabolism. Its versatile metabolism, ability to adapt to extreme conditions, low maintenance cost, and high biomass yield make it ideal for wastewater treatment and resource recovery.

WHAT IS BOKASHI COMPOSTING?

Bokashi composting is primarily breaking food waste down into a fermented mass, and the process requires very little intervention. Adding the final fermented product to the soil and aerobic compost can produce a super-fertile growth medium. It can even be done indoors.

Effective Microorganisms (EM)

Bokashi creates a symbiotic effect by combining lactic acid bacteria, yeast, and phototropic bacteria. These microorganisms have a catalytic impact on present organisms in the soil, limiting the development of harmful bacteria and supporting the development of beneficial soil biota.

Bokashi Composting

Bokashi is an intensive method of composting. Effective microorganisms (EM) support beneficial microbes that exist natively in the soil. The resulting soil becomes richer, and plants grow healthier and more resistant to diseases and harmful insects.

Since the widespread introduction of EM, Bokashi is generally made using molasses, water, EM, and wheat bran (rice hulls, or even sawdust). It can use aerobic or anaerobic inoculation to produce the compost. Once a starter culture is made, it can be extended indefinitely, like yogurt and sourdough starters.

In home-composting applications, kitchen waste is placed into a container sealed with an airtight lid. These scraps are then inoculated with a Bokashi EM mix. The mix usually takes the form of a carrier bulking agent such as rice hulls, wheat bran, or sawdust. The bulking agent has been inoculated with concentrated effective microorganisms.

BOKASHI COMPOSTING

Bokashi is the Japanese word for "ferment." Professor Teruo Higa, a professor at the Department of Horticulture at the University of the Ryukyus, Okinawa, Japan, expands on EM thus:

The technology was initiated in the 1980s in Japan and was based on developing sustainable organic food systems. The success achieved in this field – both in crops and livestock, including aquaculture, led to its expansion into industries and even health.

In the 1980s, Dr. Higa reported that a combination of around 80 different microorganisms could positively influence decomposing organic matter, causing it to revert to a *life-promoting* value. Effective microorganisms are explained by invoking the 'dominance principle.' Dr. Higa proposed that microorganisms can be divided into three categories:

- Positive microorganisms – responsible for regeneration
- Harmful microorganisms – accountable for decomposition and degeneration
- Opportunist microorganisms

According to Dr. Higa, the ratio between harmful and positive microorganisms is critical because opportunist microorganisms follow the dominant trend – more good, and they become good. EM, initially proposed as a soil enrichment regime, has expanded its usability to include infection control, stain removal, and pesticide.

HOW TO MAKE BOKASHI BRAN

Up to now, we've paid a lot of attention to the EM part of Bokashi composting. This is because EM is the *magic juice*. But EM is just a microorganism-rich liquid that can be used to inoculate bulking agents that will better (and more economically) spread the effective microorganisms. The bulking agents are usually carbon-based, but you can also use EM on cat litter to control odors and bacteria.

Depending on your personality type, you may wish to purchase Bokashi bran, or you may want to make your own. Making your own Bokashi bran is uncomplicated and economical.

Essentially, you want to expand your EM's availability. Your effective microorganisms need a place to live, transport, and eat. Effective microorganisms need a material that offers a high surface area and is rich in carbon. Their most common substrate is wheat bran, but you can also use rice hulls, shredded paper, or untreated sawdust.

Microorganisms need water for mobility, which allows the EM to fully permeate the substrate. It would be better to use unchlorinated water. Effective microorganisms consume carbohydrates. Adding molasses, sugary water, or beer will help your microorganisms grow and multiply. Molasses is good because it is inexpensive and rich in other minerals. Sugary water is rich in carbohydrates, and beer contains uric acid – a nitrogen source.

Bokashi Bran Ingredients

To make your Bokashi bran, you need the following ingredients and equipment. The rule of thumb is that you need a quarter of your wheat bran weight in water.

Helpful Conversions

- 1 gallon is equal to 19 cups (19.2152 exactly)
- 1 gallon of water weighs 8.345 pounds

Ingredients and Tools

- 12.5 pounds of wheat bran (or rice hulls)
- 1 cup of Bokashi EM-1 (NOT EMA)
- 1 cup of molasses (or alternative)
- 60 fl. oz. of warm water (120 degrees Fahrenheit) – preferably unchlorinated or de-chlorinated
- Large mixing container (not washed in antibacterial detergent – wiped with diluted EM-1)
- A potato masher
- A plastic sheet big enough to cover the container top. While many suggest using a refuse sack, don't use antibacterial versions)

Bokashi Bran Recipe

Step 1

Add the wheat bran or rice hulls to the mixing bowl. If you buy wheat bran in bulk, it ought to cost you just over 50¢ per pound. Rice hulls are a bit more expensive. Wheat bran for worm farms is also a suitable alternative. Because we want maximum surface area, the finer, the better. Because Bokashi composting is anaerobic, we don't have concerns about compacting.

Step 2

Mix the Molasses, EM-1, and water. Your water is one-quarter of the weight of your wheat bran (12.5 divided by 4 = 3.125 pounds of water) – which is 60 fluid ounces or just more than 7 cups. Remember, warm water (not hot) stimulates your effective microorganisms activity and makes it easier to dissolve the molasses (or treacle).

Step 3

Add your fluids to the dry ingredients. Thoroughly mix your water mixture in with the wheat bran, ensuring that you have no dry bits. If your bran stock is super dry, add additional water a little at a time. Do not let your bran mix get too hydrated. It has to be evenly damp – not wet, not dry.

Step 4

Remove as much air as you can. Use the potato masher to press your mix to the bottom of your bucket, removing air from the bucket. Use your plastic sheet (it could be a refuse bag) to isolate your mix from getting oxygen – pressing it slightly in around the edges. The effective microorganisms in EM-1 do best in anaerobic conditions.

Step 5

Store in an airtight container for a month in summer and three months in winter. It is best to leave the newly manufactured Bokashi bran untouched for a minimum of at least a month, stored in a warm place, and hidden from direct sunlight. The longer it stays in anaerobic conditions, the more your effective microorganisms get an opportunity to grow and multiply.

At some point, they will run out of carbohydrates, at which point they will become dormant (not die).

Step 6 (optional)

Optionally, you can **dry the Bokashi bran** mix and store it for up to two years. You can do this by spreading the fully inoculated mixture on a tarp in the shade to dry it out. When the color turns darker, and it smells sweet and sour, fermentation is completed.

If the weather doesn't permit this, you can dry it in batches in an oven with the door open and the temperature set to as low as possible. You do not want to heat your

Bokashi bran higher than 120 degrees Fahrenheit.

Finally

Finally, you have a supply of homemade Bokashi bran to use in your Bokashi bin. Every time you add kitchen scraps to the container, spread some Bokashi bran over the top.

Your effective organisms in the inoculated bran will break organic matter down and create a fermented mass. Feel free to add meat, bones, peels, and eggshells – your EM will break it all down safely.

TROUBLE SHOOTING PROBLEMS WHEN MAKING BOKASHI

During the process of fermentation, your Bokashi bin content will create a range of bacteria and fungi spores. The effective organisms that include lactic acid bacteria (yogurt), yeast, and a form of algae, will prevent the content from putrefying (rotting). There should be no foul smells.

What Could go Wrong?

Below is a list of things that may be cause for disaster.

Too Much Oxygen in the Process

It is impossible to eliminate oxygen, but you want to keep it below 6%. Your effective microorganisms are allergic to oxygen. To do their job, you need to keep the bin closed and expel the air from the mix daily.

I use a potato masher dedicated to the job. After adding your food scraps and covering them with a layer of Bokashi bran, press the mass down for the liquids to drain into the catch-tray and expel the air.

Water Accumulation in the Process

The step above is essential to minimize both air **and** water. To ensure no liquids accumulate in the bin's bottom area, invest in a suitable Bokashi bin. You can cut its running cost by making your own bran, but don't skimp on the Bokashi bin and EM-1.

A suitable Bokashi bin has a false-bottom topped with a grid that separates the fermenting materials from the drained liquids. This section is then fitted with a tap for you to drain the juices, which should be done every second day.

Bokashi Bran Not Effectively Inoculated

If you make your own Bokashi bran, you risk it not being effectively inoculated with effective microorganisms. Explanations as to why this happens are myriad.

To ensure your process is effective, make smaller batches initially. Document the adjustments you make to the mix. Record the day's ambient temperature, humidity, and any other applicable variants.

Once you have a working pattern, stick to the basic plan, only making small changes and noting changes in your fermenting process. Composting is both a science and an art.

Scrap Pieces Too Big

It is advisable to increase the surface area of your kitchen scraps where possible. Try not to add pieces that are bigger than a cubic inch (medium button mushroom). Of course, you won't need to chop up your scrap bones, but these may take longer to break down.

In my final fermented mass, I sometimes get bones and avocado peels. Still, these readily break down once I add the Bokashi bin content to my soil mix.

Effective Microorganisms Can't Get to Their Food Source

For the EM to do their work, they need to be put at the worksite. When you add your kitchen scraps, it may be a good idea to sprinkle them with Bokashi bran before you add them.

Alternatively, add a layer of about an inch or two of kitchen scraps, and add two tablespoons of Bokashi bran to the mix. Stir the top layer to spread the bran as much as possible. You want the scraps to be lightly covered with Bokashi bran to speed up the fermentation and limit odors and pathogens.

Remember to press the mix down to remove any air and juices before sealing the lid again.

HOW WILL I KNOW IF MY BOKASHI BIN FERMENTATION PROCESS IS FAILING?

Below is a list of indicators that you need to dump your Bokashi process and start over. When starting over, do not wash your Bokashi bin with antibacterial. Instead, use a clean rag soaked a solution (1:10) of water and EM-1.

Black or green mold on top of the pile

On top of your fermenting food scraps, you will notice white fluff that looks like light cotton wool. It is mycelia, the vegetative part of fungi and bacteria. The fact that it is white indicates that your batch is healthy and the EM are effectively active.

If your spores are black or green, the batch is putrefied and needs to be dumped. There are no corrective measures that can be taken once purification has set in.

A foul smell is coming from the bin

The smell of the fermentation process is like mild cider. You are creating pickled food scraps loaded with organisms that will break the food down entirely once it's added to soil, where resident microbes will finish the work.

If there is a putrid smell, your batch has gone off. This could be a result of any of the causes listed above. Some say their Bokashi smells like vomit. I have never had a vomit-smelling batch, and my nose is super sensitive to smells.

My advice is to minimize fluid retention and trapped air pockets and maximize contact of microbes to food, as evidenced by Bokashi bran spread.

Kitchen scraps are too wet inside the bin (water wet – usually at the bottom)

Bokashi bins come fitted with a drainage tap below the false bottom (below a separator mesh). The juice (sometimes called tea) that is drained is usually quite acidic and unsuitable for some plants.

The Bokashi tea is loaded with EM, and pouring a diluted mix down your drain helps manage foul odors and clogging. For plants that like a low pH, the tea is a great booster.

These include:

- Radish
- Potato
- Sweet potato
- Parsley
- Peppers
- Rhubarb
- Blueberries
- Cranberries
- Elderberries
- Gooseberries

Ensure that water and air are expelled from the mix of kitchen scraps and EM to optimize the fermenting process. Excess water inhibits this process, as does more than 6% oxygen.

USING THE "COMPOST" FROM YOUR BOKASHI BIN

The fermented kitchen scraps from your Bokashi bin are not compost but a microorganism-enriched mass of readily decomposable matter. Follow these steps to create compost with the kitchen scraps from your Bokashi bin.

STORE THE SEALED BIN FOR TWO WEEKS BEFORE USING
Once your Bokashi bin is full, add a final layer of Bokashi bran on top of the scraps and seal the container airtight. Store it out of direct sunlight for an additional two weeks.

I have two bins for this very reason. While the one is in the final stages of fermentation, I use the second one for my kitchen scraps. Alternatively, you can keep your scraps in a container in the fridge until the bin becomes available when you'll add them to the bin. Remember to layer the kitchen scraps two inches deep and cover them with Bokashi bran.

MAKING A COMPOST FROM BOKASHI FERMENTED SCRAPS
Bokashi Trench Composting
To create a nutrient-rich garden bed, dig a trench of about a foot wide and equally deep (12 inches) and a yard long. Using your wheelbarrow, add about two-thirds of

the excavated soil and mix it with the fermented mass from the Bokashi bin.

When you open your bin, you may find it covered with white fungi spores (mycelia). This is an excellent sign that your fermented matter is healthy.

Mix the content in with the soil and use the mix to fill your trench two-thirds full. Use the remaining ground to cover the mixed compost-to-be in the trench. The covered trench may stand proud, like a mound, but that is fine.

Leave the trench for a minimum of two weeks for the final decomposition to happen, after which you can use the area as a garden bed. The Bokashi will attract other beneficial microorganisms and soil biota that will significantly improve the soil quality.

Remember the principle of minimum tillage. Every time we dig the soil up, we disturb a delicately balanced system of soil biota. The Bokashi and soil mix (and if you added any other compost, good) will create a very healthy soil food web teeming with life.

While we directly enriched only an area of a foot wide, those organisms will spread to adjacent areas if there's water that aids their mobility. By planting on the trench and up to a foot on either side of it, you have a yard-wide vegetable bed with ultra-fertile soil. Not only is the soil more fertile, but it also has better water management abilities too.

Bokashi Indoor Composting

If you live in an environment where you do not have access to your own soil, Bokashi composting is a great solution. We all have kitchen scraps that can be transformed into valuable resources no matter where we live.

Having a Bokashi bin will allow you to ferment your scraps hygienically and later convert the fermented mass into ultra-fertile potting soil. The best of it all, it can all be done indoors.

Ingredients and Tools Needed for Indoor Bokashi Composting

- An airtight 4 gallon bucket or bag (you can get commercial versions on Amazon)
- A small bag of garden soil (not potting soil, which is too coarse)
- A small bag of compost
- A mixing trowel
- A couple of newspaper sheets
- (Optional) Dry builders sand or pebbles (enough to just cover the base of the bucket)
- A large mixing bowl or tarp

Indoor Bokashi Composting Steps

Prepare your Container

Wipe your composting container (bag or bucket) with a 1:10 solution of EM-1 to remove any antibacterial residue on the inner surface. With COVID-19, the world has become super aware of microorganisms, and we're killing much more than we need to, but such are the times we live in.

Provide a Way to Absorb Excess Moisture

Line the bucket or bag with a newspaper at to bottom to absorb any fluids. (*If there's a specific article that irks your sensibilities, add it where it belongs – in the compost. It's called maximizing the benefits.)

If your mixture is very damp (it shouldn't be), add dry builders sand or pebbles under the newspaper for additional absorption.

Mix Your Compost and Garden Soil

Using your tarp or mixing bowl, combine your garden soil and compost. The addition of compost adds diverse beneficial microorganisms that the EM-rich fermented mass will activate. A tarp is a handy addition to a home, allowing you a hygienic space to work on.

Talking about hygiene: EM-1 is an excellent alternative to antibacterial sprays, solvents, and soaps. It manages pathogens effectively and can remove stains. I have switched, and it works wonders for me. I've become a compulsive EM-1 dilution sprayer and wiper.

Let's get back to the tarp and soil mix. Split the soil mix up into five parts. The reasons will become evident soon.

Mix the Soil and Bokashi

Fill the bottom of the container with a fifth of our soil mix. This part of the bucket will eventually become saturated with effective microorganisms through capillary action and gravity. It also prevents putrefaction if there is too much moisture.

Mix the content from your Bokashi bin (that has been fermenting for at least two weeks) with three-fifths of the remaining soil mix. Add this to the container before finally adding the last fifth on top.

Seal And Store For a Month Before Using Your Ultra-Fertile Potting Soil

Before closing your bucket or bag, expel all the air by pressing down on the top of the mix. If you are using one of the commercial bags, I suggest you place it on a newspaper in case there is any seepage.

Store the bag or bucket where it is not exposed to direct sunlight. If you store the bucket on your balcony exposed to ambient temperatures, the following times apply. In the summer months, your ultra-fertile potting soil ought to be ready within a month. In winter, I would leave the bucket until early spring before using it – at least six weeks.

Is Bokashi Compost Better Than Standard Composting?

Well, yes and no. Bokashi composting is neither better nor less promising than standard composting – it's just different. Below are some of the key differences between traditional composting and Bokashi composting.

Method	Key Differentiator	Benefits
Traditional Hot Composting	Focussed on allowing the proliferation of aerobic soil biota, including bacteria and fungi	Well researched and tested nitrogen conversion, pathogenic prevention, and moisture management abilities
Mold Composting	Focussed on developing fungi to break organic matter down, usually leaves	Creates hygroscopic (moisture attracting and storing) organic matter that attracts other microorganisms that benefit the soil's biota
Anaerobic Composting	The purposeful reduction of living matter to a state of decomposition. It takes longer. It attracts residential microorganisms in the soil	Processes like trench composting are hassle-free (bury-and-forget)
Fermentation Composting	Uses effective microorganisms to ferment fresh food for accelerated decomposition	Reduces the decomposition time significantly while providing control of the microorganism's specifics

Traditional Hot Composting

The compost you buy from a store or create by home composting is generally made using an aerobic process involving carbon matter, nitrogen, water, oxygen, and heat. This process is often referred to as ***hot composting*** and has proven benefits.

By ensuring latent microorganisms have moisture for mobility, oxygen for health, and nitrogen for food, and by allowing them to get hotly excited, they multiply and consume the carbon-rich organic matter. In the process, they make the nitrogen they consume available to plants (through a chain of events that includes other soil microorganisms).

If you want to maximize the benefits of the hot composting process, you will need to manage it. Ensuring the presence of moisture (to cool and to make the microorganisms mobile) and an adequate supply of oxygen (greater than 6%) requires some hands-on effort. It also requires timing, something that is less of a science than an art form.

The final product, once sufficiently cured, is loaded with microorganisms ready to bring every natural benefit to your soil and, by implication, your plants. Good compost benefits the soil's water management abilities, soil texture, and fertility. Compost tea may help control pests and diseases if sprayed on the plant's foliage.

Mold Composting

Organic matter that is rich in cellulose and lignin is best degraded by fungal activity. Composting leaves is an example. By increasing the available surface area (shredding) and adding water and nitrogen, leaves break down to create leaf mold.

The resultant leaf mold is highly hygroscopic. Put differently, leaf mold is a water magnet. Because it loves water, it is better as a soil enhancer than as mulch. Used as a mulch, it may absorb moisture from the ground to satisfy its urge.

I use leaf mold as potting soil, planting directly into it without any further enhancements. Leaves are an abundant free resource. It only takes the effort of collecting and shredding them to make tons of highly fertile potting soils.

When leave mold is mixed into soil, the resident microbes are enhanced by the presence of carbon and nitrogen, further enriching the soil.

Anaerobic Composting

Anaerobic composting is used to manufacture biofuels. With in-vessel composting, the process often opts for anaerobic conditions. It extracts the methane produced, converting it to be used as an energy source.

At a gardener's level, anaerobic composting would be path composting or trench composting. Both methods bury fresh organic material for a year, during which time local residential microorganisms will break it down. The result is a strengthened soil biota that befits both soil and plants.

Fermented Composting

The fermenting process is often, erroneously, compared to pickling your food scraps. Pickles are created using acids. Fermentation is a process performed by bacteria and fungi and involves sugars. Think of beer, wine, ginger beer, and kombucha.

It fascinates me that in China, centuries ago, they discovered the benefits of lactic acid bacteria and yeast to improve gut health with kombucha. And then, in the seventies, Dr. Higa in Japan used these two microorganisms (and purple algae) to create EM and the Bokashi concept. I wonder if the one was a seed to the other, or whether it is coincidental?

While Bokashi is often referred to as a composting process, it is the Japanese term for fermentation. The Bokashi process produces fermented kitchen food scraps. The benefit of this process is the organic waste is loaded with effective microorganisms.

Dr. Higa's proven hypothesis was that non-pathogenic (neutral) microorganisms would become beneficial if the cohort of microorganisms were inoculated with effective microorganisms. The abundance of effective microorganisms would irradicate pathogenic organisms.

So, when the fermented product is added to soil, the microorganisms in the soil are boosted "for good" to accelerate the decomposition process. What usually takes about a year to decompose in an anaerobic environment (like trench composting) can now be done in a month (if you take the fermentation process into account).

WHAT VOLUME OF COMPOST CAN BE MADE WITH BOKASHI?

The availability of food scraps is the limiting factor. In environments like restaurants and food courts where there is much wastage, Bokashi is a great option. Bulk Bokashi fermenters will require regular draining, though this can be automated.

Add a food layer and sufficient Bokashi bran to cover the scraps, inoculating the mass with EM in the process. Adding cardboard containers will not negatively affect the process. Holding containers must actively separate the fermenting scraps from water drainage, limit oxygen pockets, and must be sealable for two weeks.

To minimize the need for additional space, which for most operations are at a premium, once the bin is packed and sealed, it can be removed from the premises. Creating compost from the fermented food scraps is often done in warehouses.

In a domestic environment, the average household of three to four will fill the standard 5-gallon bin in two weeks. Such a household can produce 20 gallons (3.2 cubic feet) of compost per month. In a year, it's enough to create a fertile garden and provide fertile soil for all the house plants you could want – **all from kitchen scraps that would typically be binned**.

SUMMARY

Effective microorganisms (EM) present a whole new approach to dealing with kitchen scraps – and it's a wonderful one at that. With more than 40% of produced food going to waste, processes like Bokashi fermentation offer an opportunity to turn food wastage into ultra-fertile soil.

FAQ

Why do I have worms in my Bokashi bin?

Nature's essential insect responsible for protein decomposition is the domestic fly. They jump into action as soon as they find exposed protein, laying their eggs in neat little rows, and the hatching larvae consume the protein, breaking it down.

If you leave your drainage tap or bin open, the domestic fly will do what it's programmed to do. The result is worms in your Bokashi. The essential rules of Bokashi composting apply: minimize water, keep air out, keep the bin (and tap) closed.

Bokashi is an anaerobic process. Will I be producing methane gas?

The difference with the Bokashi is that it uses select microorganisms to ferment the food scraps. When you open the bin to add scraps, the only smell you should have is a very slight acidic smell. If there are foul odors, you have not added sufficient inoculated Bokashi bran, or the fermenting mass has not drained well. The process impedes the formation of methane gas.

Does the liquid I drain from my Bokashi bin have any value?

The fluids that drain from the fermenting food scraps contain billions of effective microorganisms. It is very nutrient-rich but is somewhat acidic and not suitable for plants that prefer alkalinity. See the plants on which the Bokashi bin juices can be used above. Dilution is advised to extend and spread the benefits.

EM has a broad range of applications, from making Bokashi to clearing up pollution. Effective microorganisms are also used to treat lakes and rivers. Nature has provided us with all that is good and can ensure its own wellbeing when not messed with. The point is, by adding EM to your drain, you offer it the means to clear blockages and reduce foul smells.

What shouldn't I add to my Bokashi bin?
- Liquids. Don't add coffee, and other drinks, juices, or frying oils or fats – but you can add the coffee grounds and tea bags or leaves.
- Food that is already off.
- Pet feces – not in the bin, but your Bokashi bran will be an excellent addition to cat litter.
- Non-organic matter – like plastic cutlery.

What will happen if I run out of Bokashi bran? Can I still add food scraps to my Bokashi bin?
Your Bokashi food fermenter bin will function well as long as you add enough Bokashi bran, limit air pockets, and minimize fluids. If you run out of Bokashi bran, keep the bin closed (make sure the tap is closed too) and use it again once you make or get more Bokashi bran. In the meantime, you can hoard your kitchen scraps in a sealed container in the fridge. Add these to the bin once you have Bokashi bran again, remembering to layer food and Bokashi bran.

I've heard that Bokashi bran has other uses. What are they?
EM is classified as a liquid microbial inoculant and has no toxicity risks for humans and animals. By mixing it with wheat bran (or rice hulls), we effectively multiply the microorganisms and extend the liquid's use.

- Adding the inoculated bran to cat litter will help control smells.
- Adding the Bokashi bran to your worm farm will boost the farm's productivity.
- You can add Bokashi bran as nesting material for hamsters, and other similar pets.
- You can use the Bokashi bran as a ground cover on white patches on your lawn.

Think of Bokashi bran as a granular form of probiotics.

ANAEROBIC COMPOSTING SUMMARY

To be technically accurate, anaerobic digestion is not a composting process. The product is not compost but rather a range of digestates. While these digestates have definite value as soil additives, they do not provide the scope of serviceability offered by aerobic compost. There are two main differences between aerobic and anaerobic composting: residual nitrogen and increased beneficial populations of microorganisms.

While anaerobic digestion has definite nitrogen production and retention advantages for the residential gardener, it fails to provide the scope of microorganisms needed to enhance soil cohesion (aggregates), added carbon matter, pH buffering, and water management.

Although their processes differ from anaerobic digestion, I included leaf mold and Bokashi composting as both are not oxygen dependent. Our accelerated leaf mold/ compost pile can be stacked once and left for six months without turning. The same goes for Bokashi fermentation and the final holding time – no oxygen required.

8. OTHER COMPOSTING PROCESSES

This chapter reviews composting methods that fall beyond the general scope of aerobic and anaerobic composting. Even so, they form an integral part of the gardener's composting skillset and are indispensable in improving the health of both plants and soil. We also review some inoculation methods that benefit the soil directly or improve your compost quality.

Covered in this Chapter:

- Vermicomposting

- Compost Teas
    o Actively Aerated Compost Tea (AACT)
    o Non-Aerated Compost Extract (NCE)

- Inocula
    o Arbuscular Mycorrhiza (AM)
    o Effective Microbes (EM)

VERMICOMPOSTING

VERMICOMPOSTING SYNOPSIS

Vermicomposting is a highly effective bio-oxidative process that involves earthworms and microorganisms working together to break down organic matter into a potent soil amendment. While I've seen operations that produce tons of worm castings, we'll focus on residential operations. Essentially, the size of your vermicomposting operation depends on available space, the amount of worm food you have available, and the time you want to spend farming worms and collecting their castings.

Vermicomposting is a non-thermophilic biological oxidation process where select earthworm species, preferably Eisenia fetida (red wigglers), enhance the conversion of organic waste to compost. Earthworms help influence the growth of specific microbial species that improve the soil's physical and chemical properties. The microbial population present in vermicompost plays an essential role in increasing crop productivity and maintaining the soil's structural stability.

VERMICOMPOST HIGHLIGHTS:

- There are approximately 9,000 earthworm species, of which seven are suitable for vermicomposting, to varying degrees.
- Vermicomposting requires high feeders. Earthworms in your garden are unsuitable for vermicomposting; use red worms (Eisenia fetida and E. Andrei) instead.
- Worms are most active in moist environments at temperatures between 55 degrees Fahrenheit and 85 degrees Fahrenheit. Their living quarters must be dark and have enough air. Worms try to escape unsuitable environments.
- Earthworms are hermaphrodites, but two worms are required for reproduction, exchanging sperm as they lay alongside each other. Both get covered in the process.
- Conditions permitting, your worm population can double every two months.
- Cocoons take four to six weeks to emerge, and the two to five worms from each cocoon take a further six to eight weeks to mature. Cocoons take longer to release the worms in colder conditions.
- Worms require some sand grains to strengthen their consumption capacities.
- Generally, vermicompost is equivalent to a 3:3:3 fertilizer with higher nitrate (NO_3).
- Vermicompost is rich in microorganisms, as worms use bacteria in their gut to process food.

- A carbon-rich diet will increase fungi populations for regions that require better water retention.
- Worm castings are rich in enzymes.
- Worm mucus helps soil particles form aggregates.
- Vermicompost improves root penetration, water usage, and nutrient availability as a product of improved soil structure.
- Desirable microorganisms thrive, increasing resilience against pests and diseases.
- Earthworms feed on decaying organic matter and microorganisms, like nematodes. Underground, they eat bacteria, algae, fungi, and nematodes, releasing the minerals consumed by microorganisms into the soil.
- In worm bins, they consume kitchen waste and limited yard waste.
- Avoid
    - Animal products and by-products (cheese, yogurt, etc.)
    - Some citrus fruits (orange peels and pineapples)
    - Glossy paper
    - Onions and garlic
    - Salt
    - Oily substances

- Advisable food for your worm farm
    - Fruits and vegetable scraps
    - Coffee grounds and filters (snip filters into smaller parts)
    - Grains – bread, crackers, cereals, even if they are moldy or stale
    - Leaves
    - Eggshells
    - Paper products. Shred cardboard
    - Grass clippings if not treated with pesticides or herbicides.

- Worms live for about one year, and because their bodies are 90% water, their dead bodies dry up and become part of the compost. The cycle of life and death is seamless and unnoticeable, with populations remaining in balance with their environment.
- Approximately 800-1,000 mature worms (or one pound) can consume about half a pound of organic material each day.
- Bins can be customized depending on the volume of food scraps used to manufacture the castings.
- Useable castings take approximately three to four months to produce, depending on the bin size.

BACKGROUND TO CREATING A WORM BIN

Worm composting provides a convenient method for recycling kitchen scraps into a nutrient-rich product. Properly managed worm composting is almost odorless and can actually reduce odors associated with kitchen scraps mixed in with garbage. Combined with Bokashi fermentation, vermicomposting can produce a highly fertile soil amendment.

Vermicomposting can be done in a variety of containers. Scaled operations generally use raised wooden structures utilizing vertical or horizontal feeding. In horizontal feeding, fresh scraps or compost is added in strips adjacent to worm populations, creating a progressive linear sheet of vermicompost. In vertical feeding, a layer of compost is added on top of the worm population, creating horizontal layers of vermicompost. The end product in horizontal feeding is a flat surface, almost like a pool table, of vermicompost containing abundant worms.

You can use old wash tubs, shopping crates, plastic utility tubs, or polystyrene containers for a worm farm at a residential scale. You can also manufacture a wood crate but *avoid using cedar* as it contains antimicrobial elements. There is a range of commercially available containers specially designed for vermicomposting – I would advise that these be bought from worm farmers and not plastic tool manufacturers. Essentially, you want a container with a lid, ample ventilation for air and evaporation, and sufficient space. It's also advisable for beginners to provide drainage holes at the bottom of their bin. If you do, place your bin on a catch tray to collect seepage from the system. This liquid erroneously referred to as vermicomposting tea, could be toxic to plants – depending on the cause of the leachate.

The three essential attributes of your container are its depth, floor size, and construction. The **depth** should be between 8 and 16 inches deep. This is because your red wrigglers are continuously moving toward fresh food and require separate bedding. An interesting fact: mature worms allow younger worms to get the best fresh food, always remaining a layer or two below. Maybe it's a survival adaptation to avoid becoming prey for larger animals.

An easy way to calculate the required container **floor space** is to provide one square foot for every pound of food scrap your household produces a week. It might be a good idea to weigh your daily scraps for a week or two to get the average daily food scrap production. By multiplying the average daily scraps by seven, you can determine your weekly average. Another way of getting a guesstimate of the required size is that you need a square foot of container floor space for every person in the household.

At the minimum 8 inches deep:

Width*	Length*	Depth	Cubic Inches	US Gallons	lbs. Food/ Week	Worms Required
12	24	8	2304	9.97	2.00	571
18	18	8	2592	11.22	2.25	643
15	25	8	3000	12.99	2.60	744
18	24	8	3456	14.96	3.00	857
18	36	8	5184	22.44	4.50	1286

* Important aspect – floor space

According to the EPA[4], 42.8 million tons (or 68%) of food ended up in landfills or combustion facilities. So, don't be shocked when you weigh those food scraps. Instead of a larger bin, opt for multiple smaller bins – big bins are a bother to move and clean. A 10-gallon styrofoam bin is ideal – it is insulated, lightweight, and generally deep enough. Also, creating ventilation holes is easy.

Approximately 800-1,000 mature worms (or one pound) can consume about half a pound of organic material each day (3.5 pounds per week). Bins can be customized depending on the volume of food scraps used to manufacture the castings. Useable castings of sufficient quantity take approximately three to four months to produce, depending on the bin size.

PLACING YOUR VERMICOMPOSTING CONTAINER

Your worms are optimally productive at temperatures between 55 and 85 degrees Fahrenheit. Avoid extreme temperature fluctuations. Generally, worm farmers keep their containers in the basement, but find what works for you. An alternative is to keep the container outside when temperatures are above 50 degrees Fahrenheit, but beware of other strange insects entering the bin. You can adjust your bin's design to meet the environmental challenges. Because vermicomposting is relatively odorless, you can leave it in a prominent place, too – just decorate it and refer to it as productive art.

---

4   *https://www.epa.gov/recycle/reducing-wasted-food-home*

Unlike Bokashi bins that can be topped up daily, vermicomposting bins should only have food added weekly. If your worm bin develops an odor, it indicates that you are overfeeding your worms. You have three options: wait for the worm population to catch up with available food, reduce food supply, or buy more worms.

HOW TO CREATE A SUCCESSFUL VERMICULTURE BIN

Worms

There are more than 90,000 earthworm types. The Gippsland earthworm is an Australian variant that grows up to 10 feet in length and an inch in diameter. Six variants are suitable for vermicomposting:

- Red Wiggler (Eisenia fetida)
- Red Worm (Lumbricus rubellus)
- Red Tiger (Eisenia andrei)
- Blue Worm (Perionyx excavatus)
- African Nightcrawlers (Eudrilus eugeniae)
- European Nightcrawlers (Eisenia hortensis)

Red wigglers (Eisenia fetida) are your best option for creating your first worm farm. They do best in temperate, dark, and moist conditions, with minimal disturbance, and they operate in the top 6 inches of their bedding. They want to be left to feed on organic waste or compost, breed, and create worm castings. Of particular interest to them (and the quality of your worm castings) is a balanced diet of moldy fruit scraps, shredded cardboard, leaf mold, tea bags, and coffee grounds. Reproduction rates are accelerated on a high-moisture, sugary diet. Your worms are light-shy, so it is ideal for keeping them in the shade, in a cupboard, under the sink, or in a dim room. Ensure that the cupboards provide sufficient ventilation.

Container

While I'm an avid advocate for freedom of choice, please allow me to influence your choice of bins. If you can repurpose a plastic or polystyrene container, please do so. Polystyrene takes 500 to 800 years to decompose, and polypropylene takes 20 to 30 years to decompose. If we can keep these

materials out of landfills, we're doing our bit towards a more sustainable world. Rather make one yourself from available materials than buy a plastic-tiered worm composting farm with limited efficacy.

Your worm bin can be made of plastic, wood, or Styrofoam. Again, to ensure the population of healthy microorganisms, avoid cedar wood. Remember to ensure the container can be closed or covered to limit light and prevent the worms from escaping and other insects from entering. Also, there needs to be enough ventilation on the sides and drainage at the bottom. The worm bin needs to be propped up off the ground for the bottom drainage to work. Ideally, you want nothing less than a 10-gallon container to start with. If you need more bin floor space, consider a larger bin, or multiple bins.

A gallon is 231 cubic inches. A bin floor size of 18 x 36 inches and a depth of 8 inches is sufficient for approximately a pound of worms able to consume about 4.5 pounds of food scraps a week – the average household's food scrap production.

Preparing a Container
- Using the suggested 18 by 36 inch Styrofoam container (minimum 8 inches deep, ideally 12 to 16 inches), use a serrated knife to cut a half-inch slot about an inch-and-a-half from the bottom on the narrow (18 inch) sides.

- The slot should provide the worms with sufficient aeration and should be about 8 to 12 inches long – parallel to the base.

- Create a 6 inch square slot in the center of the lid as well.

- Cover any holes in the bin with a non-metallic fly-screen (geotextile material). You can attach rust-proof fine netting on the inside using a glue gun. Some glues react with polystyrene, but a glue gun works well. You only need to attach it at the corners as the weight of the bedding will prevent gaps from forming at the edges. The netting must be fine enough to prevent worms from escaping yet permeable enough for unrestricted airflow. Metallic netting will deteriorate in wet and acidic environments.

- While some will advise you to create holes at the bottom for drainage, I will show you how to avoid leachate forming so holes are not needed.

- Do not use a transparent bin – it allows too much light in. Avoid direct sunlight if you use a black bin, as the bin will overheat, killing your worms.

Bedding

In most minds, bedding implies a surface **upon** which worms live. Bedding is actually the environment *in* which the worms live and **under** which you bury their food. You can only have too little bedding, not too much. The bin's base can be covered with a combination of products, including shredded cardboard, newspaper, coconut coir, peat moss, and aerobic compost.

If you're using decomposable materials, ensure a higher carbon content to slow the process down and limit heat generation. The depth is generally insufficient for heat generation if ventilation is adequate. An essential element of the bedding is sufficient moisture – moist but not wet. Shredded newspaper about an inch thick is excellent at the bottom to absorb additional moisture. Coconut coir is an excellent option to add as it keeps moisture content sufficiently high yet contained. Adding compost also benefits the environment with microorganisms – an essential part of the vermicomposting process.

Bedding provides worms with an environment that is comfortable, safe, and away from their food and castings. The food layer can be dangerous and kill them as excess food may not get eaten and start to rot. Depending on the environment, the decomposing food may heat up, become acidic, or release a lot of water. Provide a lot of bedding material when setting up your bin so your worms can take refuge, rest, and reproduce.

The created environment must be moist but still absorb any additional moisture, be aerated, be rich in carbon, and any added compost must be stable. Compost in the bedding will help regulate pH levels, populate the environment with beneficial microorganisms, and act as a moisture-absorbing material. Adding some form of grit is necessary as it aids the worms' digestive systems. Finely ground eggshells help balance the pH and act as grit. Adding a little soil also helps.

Bedding Should Provide your Worms With:
- A clean home and protection from light
- Strategically added Bokashi bran will absorb excess moisture from the food scraps, preventing smelly anaerobic conditions
- Sufficient airflow – shredded cardboard helps

- Some warmth in winter – add an additional layer of bedding material on top
- New bins need a minimum of 6 inches bedding material to provide a safe place to retreat
- Cover for food that is added to prevent fruit flies
- You will create a bedding sandwich for your worms. The top and bottom bedding layers will be at least 4 inches thick, in between which you will add the weekly food supply.

Suggested Bedding Materials

- Leaf mold
- Stable compost
- Aged coffee grounds
- Tea leaves
- Shredded paper that has been presoaked in water
- Coconut coir
- Shredded, presoaked cardboard
- Bokashi bran

A mixture of these provides an ideal environment as each has its added benefits. The moisture content should be between 50% and 60%. This means that if you squeeze the bedding in your fist, moisture is visible between your fingers, but none (maybe one drop) drips out.

Over time, the bedding becomes food and needs to be topped up. A good practice is to add dry bedding to cover high-moisture food scraps. Bokashi bran works well for this.

Adding Worms

You can order your red wigglers from several worm farmers who sell online. Be careful of invasive species, such as the Asian Jumping Worm, marketed as Georgia or Alabama Jumper. Red wigglers are generally sold by weight and the cost, at the time of going to press, is in the region of $60.00 per pound (1,000 mature worms – 6,000 hatchlings). The general assumption is that worms eat the equivalent of half their weight *per*

day. A pound of worms will eat half their weight in food scraps (and their bedding) a day, or 3.5 pounds per week.

MANAGING YOUR BIN

Aeration

Vermicomposting is a mesophilic process that relies on passive aeration. Bins need to provide a flow of air, with heat able to escape from the upper part of the bin. Ventilation holes at the lower part of the bin allow fresh air to be drawn in and through the material. Earthworms breathe through their skin. Your bedding also needs air to prevent anaerobic conditions and the resulting odorous stench.

Temperatures

Mesophilic organisms function at temperatures between 50 degrees Fahrenheit and 105 degrees Fahrenheit. Worms prefer temperatures between these two extremes, 55 degrees Fahrenheit to 85 degrees Fahrenheit without sudden fluctuations. If you're using dark-colored bins, direct sunlight can cause them to overheat. Ensure that your bins are located where moderate temperatures prevail. If you're unsure, check the bin's bedding temperature weekly.

If you're using a Styrofoam container, heating is more controllable. Suppose your container is made of any other material. In that case, I suggest you get a Styrofoam piece to cover the container if it stands outside to reduce heating. Fish merchants often have these in abundance, so try them for some (and prevent them from going to the trash).

Food

One of the most typical errors in vermicomposting is the anthropomorphism of the worm – attributing human characteristics to worms. Humans tend to eat at least once a day. Worms thrive when their environment remains stable, and feeding them weekly suits them (and us) best. If the food added cannot be consumed in a week, rotting sets in. If they consume the provided food within

a couple of days, their population will drop to match the food supply. A balance between the two needs to be maintained, where the food is almost entirely consumed when you add fresh food scraps. Feeding locations should alternate between corners or sides (depending on volume).

Moisture

Bedding needs to be kept moist but not wet – worms are not aquatic. If ambient temperatures are causing excessive evaporation, use a spray bottle to humidify the bedding, but avoid disturbing the worms too often. Alternatively, add fresh, moist bedding. If the bed is too moist, add Bokashi bran or other dry materials mixed in to absorb the excess moisture.

Bedding

Over time, the worms will consume the bedding. When the bedding layer drops below 4 inches, add additional fresh, moist bedding. The bottom layer of bedding should not be less than 4 inches deep, so add up to 6 inches and replenish each time it drops below the 4 inch level. Earthworms have a gizzard and five "hearts." The gizzard needs some grit to function optimally, so adding ground eggshells, coffee grounds, or fine sand helps digestion and mobility. Vermiculite or perlite is also commonly added to aid mobility.

Remember that your bedding will settle and be shredded, so adding extra bedding fortnightly will help compensate for lost depth. If you're using newspaper, lay it on the lawn, spray it, and leave it to soak for about 15 minutes. You can also soak pages in a tub before tearing them into strips.

Extended Absence

If you're planning to be away for longer than a week, add moist bedding and thin layers of food (to avoid anaerobic conditions) and cover the top with a thick layer of bedding. Using longer-lasting foods such as a pieced whole apple or potato helps extend the food supply safely. Sprinkling some raisins and/or cereals also helps provide food that won't promote anaerobic conditions. If it's summertime, add some additional moisture to the bedding.

Pests

Common pests are fruit flies and lizards. Fruit flies can be controlled by ensuring added food is covered by bedding or Bokashi bran. Controlling lizards requires that you restrict their access to the bin, and you can do this by ensuring your bin can be fully closed without any gaps.

HARVESTING VERMICOMPOST

Worms live in your bin and feed on the food and bedding you provide. If the worms' bedding is healthy, additional microorganisms are contained in it that contribute to the shredding and organic breakdown. Over time, most of the bedding is indistinguishable from worm castings. This indicates that you need to harvest the contents and create a fresh start for the worms.

Vertical Harvesting

As stated earlier, there are horizontal and vertical harvesting and feeding methods. In longer bins, it's easier to harvest vertically. This is done by attracting most worms to one edge of the container by concentrating feeding on that side for about a month. Over a month, the worms will migrate to that side, leaving the other half less populated. This allows you to harvest the compost from the vacated side without disturbing the worms.

You might want to use corrugated cardboard shaped to the inner profile of the bin to divide the bin when harvesting. Once the board is inserted vertically in the center of the bin, remove all the material from the less populated side. You may find that there are still some worms in the removed vermicompost. If you, like I, want to salvage these worms, create little piles of the vermicompost. The worms, repelled by the light, will migrate to the center as you remove the outer layers.

Sieve the vermicompost to remove any organic matter not yet processed and any stray worms. What remains is pure black gold, high in everything that makes soil healthy and rich in minerals. There is no comparative composting process that produces a richer product.

Refill the empty half with a fresh 6 inch layer of bedding, but add only a little food until the worms reestablish themselves and stabilize. Cover the food with a minimum of 4 inches of bedding. When you remove the cardboard separator, you will have a mass migration of worms toward the new facilities – happy worms. Wait another month before repeating the process to harvest the other half. Harvesting is generally every four to five months.

Horizontal Harvesting

Vertical harvesting is only suitable for longer beds where worms can migrate towards food, leaving harvestable vermicompost in their wake. In large-scale operations, this is often a continuous process if space permits. The gap between the two sides fails to provide a safe middle in smaller bins. Here horizontal harvesting is needed – the removal of everything all at once.

In horizontal feeding, across the width of the container, you will notice that over time, you'll see less bedding and more compost in your bin. The bin can be harvested after three to five months when the bin content is mostly compost. Stop feeding the worms for about two weeks, then remove the entire bin content and place it in smaller heaps on a tarp to harvest. Again, the light will cause the worms to migrate to the center, away from the light. As you remove the outer layers of the heaps, you'll be able to reclaim your worms.

Remember not to sterilize the bin or wipe it with an antibacterial solution. If you wish to clean it, use an EM solution to wipe it out. The effective microorganisms in EM will eliminate odors and create a sanitized, stable environment for microorganisms and worms. Reconstitute your bin as before with layers of bedding and reintroduce your worms. Allow them to settle for a week before feeding them again.

Sieve the vermicompost to remove any organic matter not yet processed and any stray worms. What remains is pure black gold, high in everything that makes soil healthy and rich in minerals. There is no comparative composting process that produces a richer product. Store the harvested vermicompost out of direct light in an airtight container.

USING WORM CASTINGS IN YOUR GARDEN

Worm castings are a slow-release nitrogen-rich fertilizer balanced with other essential minerals – generally equivalent to 3:3:3 NPK. You can safely spread it around potted plants, vegetables, and flowing plants. If you sift it finely, adding it to your lawn would replace your usual nitrogen needs. You can also incorporate it into the soil around shrubs and trees.

It's up to you whether you want to use your compost right away or store it for the gardening season. Vermicompost can be added directly to potting soil or garden soil as a soil amendment. This makes nutrients more accessible to plants. It's possible to top dress your indoor or outdoor plants with the compost. You can also create a nutrient-loaded compost tea by straining the vermicompost in an aerated water tank for 24 hours. Don't confuse the leachate from the bottom of a poorly managed bin with composting tea. The leachate is loaded with nitrogen and should always be diluted and used with care. I advise that you test it on a single plant, review the reaction over a couple of days, and proceed if safe. Use leachate with caution, as it has the risk of poisoning your plants.

COMPOST TEAS

As described in **Chapter 2 – Why Composting**, plants require 17 nutrients to survive. Artificial applications of the primary nutrients (nitrogen, phosphorous, and potassium) have long been promoted as the de facto route to crop yield increases. The use of synthetic fertilizers, pesticides, herbicides, and fumigants is supported by billion-dollar marketing campaigns. At ground level, though, the nutritional level of fresh produce is dropping.

Farmers find that input costs and volumes are escalating year-on-year, with diminishing yields. Increasingly farmers are turning to the sciences for solutions. Finally, the emergent appreciation of the role of soil biology in agriculture is affording the sector a turn-around strategy. The notable successes of grand-scale farmers as they move towards more sustainable practices has sparked investment for further research of the role of soil biota in crop production.

As the familiarity with the benefits of composting expands, extending its application is fast becoming the next generalist frontier. A growing number of gardeners are turning to water solutions of compost as a more natural method of boosting their plants' resilience, health, and productivity. Compost is the primary host of an assortment of microorganisms, enzymes, and minerals. It can significantly benefit the soil it's added to.

Pesticides, herbicides, and fumigants are increasingly recognized as counter-productive, killing a range of beneficial microorganisms. Their application kills both the bad and the good. In the absence of beneficial microorganisms, the soil biota cannot increase water retention, stabilize pH, fight pathogens, and improve cation-exchange capacity. While the general application of compost has enormous benefits, the specific needs of the soil (and plants) could be addressed if the broad diversity of microorganisms and pathogens were known.

While most gardeners are happy with the benefits compost provides the soil, studies show that those benefits can be extended to the rest of the plant. Aerobic microorganisms, primarily bacteria, fungi, nematodes, and protozoa, can be hosted in water for short periods – if the water is well aerated and agitated. In addition, the populations of either bacteria or fungi can be boosted through feeding regimes, depending on the application need. The water in which these microorganisms are hosted is referred to as actively aerated compost tea (AACT).

Healthy compost produces healthy AACT. Healthy AACT extends the benefits of compost:

- Beneficial microorganisms improve the surface protection of plant foliage. The attached microorganisms can defend the plant against disease-causing organisms.
- The representative microorganisms from the compost offer similar soil nutrition benefits – pH buffering, nutrient distribution, aggregate formation, aeration, water retention, etc.
- Microorganisms increase the nutrient availability where it's needed – at the roots. The soil food web's predator-prey interactions increase nutrient availability at the right time and at the right place – according to the plant's needs.
- Beneficial microorganisms can neutralize the impact of chemical-based pesticides and herbicides.
- Beneficial microorganisms reduce the loss of moisture from the leaf surface.
- Microorganisms improve tilth and soil structure – an exclusive soil biota function.

Compost tea contains all the soluble nutrients extracted from the compost and representative bacteria, fungi, protozoa, and nematodes. The compost quality used in compost tea is an essential factor in the tea's efficacy. It stands to reason that if the microorganisms and nutrients are absent in the source compost, they will not be present in the tea either. However, the populations of either bacteria or fungi can be boosted by adding food that will stimulate their individual growth. Humic acid is known to boost fungi growth, and molasses will boost the bacterial population.

Brewing an effective composting tea is dependent on several factors. Like most living organisms, including you and I, if the needs of the microorganisms are met, they thrive. Making compost tea is an evolving science, and different approaches have been developed to fully satisfy the needs of select organisms. By closely monitoring the brewing environment, beneficial microorganisms can be kept alive and helped to thrive. Factors that influence the outcome are:

- The brewing temperature
- The added foods
- The levels of oxygenation during production
- The quality and microbial composition of the compost used
- The time microorganisms are immersed in water

It's essential to remember that we're working with oxygen-dependent aerobic microorganisms. These organisms are essential to the soil, allow plants to grow unimpeded, and act as defenders of the realm. Merely soaking compost in water overnight is a good way to make humus-colored water, not compost tea. To transfer the microorganisms from the stabilized compost to water, the water environment must have at least 5.5ppm oxygen.

Anything less might be counter-productive, producing microbes that could be detrimental to the plants and soil. The bacteria responsible for diseases in humans are almost exclusively anaerobic. The added beneficial microorganisms are ousted by pathogenic microorganisms in low-oxygen teas. This scenario is less likely if your thermophilic process during composting was unquestionably effective.

Effective compost tea, like effective compost, is location-specific. The best compost is produced by gardeners or farmers using local materials. This is because the organisms in a local system are best equipped to manage the requirements of the local pedosphere. Similarly, compost-tea-making should ideally be localized using locally made compost. This is the best option, but not an absolute necessity.

If buying compost tea, remember that the shelf-life is exceptionally short (about 6 hours). If buying compost tea, your best option is to buy the compost and microorganism food and brew it at home.

COMPOST TEA VARIATIONS

Actively Aerated Compost Tea (AACT)
- An aerated brew of unchlorinated water and compost extract
- It is wholly representative of the nutrients and microorganisms in the original compost
- Added food for targeted microbial growth

Non-Aerated Compost Extract (NCE)
- A water-based extract from compost that has not been actively aerated in solution
- It may contain some of the compost microorganisms
- No added food to promote microbial growth
- Soluble nutrients and enzymes are present if used soon after making
- Very time-sensitive due to lack of aeration
- Rich in humic acid

Actively aerated compost tea is aerated using a bubbler, blower, or any other device to force oxygen-laden air into the liquid containing a bag of compost extract. Alternatively, compost extracts are only occasionally stirred to re-suspend solid materials that have settled to the bottom. This process is not actively aerated.

MAKING ACTIVE AERATED COMPOST TEA (AACT)

Resources Required:
- About a 7 gallon bucket with a cloth cover
- Air pump (aquarium air pump will do)
- A length of tubing to fit the air pump – long enough to feed air into the bottom of the bucket
- Aquarium air stones or bubblers
- 5 gallons of dechlorinated water (rainwater is suitable)
- 3 cups of finely sieved compost
- A porous bag – compost teabags are available online. Alternatively, use a sock

Directions:
- Start aerating the water in the bucket.
- Put mature compost in the bag or sock, attach it to a weight, and place the bag and weight in the bucket.
- To remove air from the compost bag, gently massage it.
- Allow the bag containing water to be aerated for 24 hours.
- If you use the AACT in a sprayer, you will need to filter the liquid before using it – a cheesecloth will be adequate.
- Use the liquid within an hour after aeration stops.

MAKING NON-AERATED COMPOST EXTRACT (NCE)

Resources Required:
- About a 7 gallon bucket with a cloth cover
- 5 gallons of dechlorinated water (rainwater is suitable)
- 3 cups of finely sieved compost in a porous bag – compost teabags are available online. Alternatively, a sock or stocking will work
- An implement to stir with

Directions
- Place the compost-filled bag in the water.
- Help your tea draw by stirring the water and massaging the bag of compost.
- Repeat the above action twice a day for the next 7 days.
- When done, filter through a cheesecloth so as not to block your sprayer nozzles.
- Use the liquid as compost, drenching the soil around plants and spraying on foliage.

COMPOSTING TEA REVIEW

I'm personally a fan of the AACT method. With the extended, non-aerated method, I imagine the microorganisms drowning, slowly growing weaker, until all I'm stirring are unresponsive microbodies. With the AACT method, my little divers get a chance to take a gulp of air, have plenty of additional food, and are even reproducing. This sounds like a better plan to me.

But the proof is in the pudding, as they say. There is no set recipe for compost teas, and the above ones are mere guidelines. As a master gardener, you will develop what works for you, your soil, and your plants. If you really want to be effective, find a lab that can analyze your soil – not for chemical content, but rather microbial diversity and population. That way, you can know what is abundant and in deficit. Diversity rules the earth – literally. The more diverse your population and balanced the predator-prey systems are, the healthier your soil and happier your plants are.

Speaking of diversity, we know the thermophilic phase of composting reaches temperatures that are unsuitable for many fungi species. While evolution has provided them with a survival strategy, it remains much easier to end with a batch of compost high in bacteria than fungi populations. Using the initial compost, AACT offers gardeners an easy way to boost the fungi populations in the soil.

Bacteria thrive on sugars, and fungi thrive on proteins. By adding a tiny amount of protein (fish hydrolysis or humic acid), you can boost your fungi population in the tea, and therefore the soil. The amount is approximately 2 teaspoons to 5 gallons of water. Remember to always use dechlorinated water when working with anything microbial. You can also fill a bucket of water from the tap and leave it in the sun for a day to neutralize the chlorine (or add some ascorbic acid).

Worthy of a special mention is the manufacturing of AACT using vermicompost. Vermicompost is the most nutritious version of compost, especially if the food supply is predominantly aerobic compost and leaf mold.

INOCULA

There is a growing understanding of soil biology that bodes well for the sustainability of our planet. For scientists with access to technologies to accurately evaluate the composition of soil biota, the process of soil health improvement is much easier. Gardeners, on the other hand, are often left with a process of trial and error. There is a lot of valuable information online. Still, many click-bait gung-ho operators tarnish the sector with a lot of misinformation or partial truths. Organizations such as the Rodale Institute[5] and Dr. Elaine Ingham's Soil Food Web Inc.[6] have made invaluable contributions to our understanding of the soil food web and organic processes. The information below refers to work being done by the Rodale Institute and other organizations.

---

5   *https://rodaleinstitute.org*

6   *https://www.soilfoodweb.com*

ARBUSCULAR MYCORRHIZAL (AM) FUNGI INOCULATION

Mycorrhizal

A forest is a unique system of diversity from which we can learn much. Fungi usually grow close to other plants. Underground, fungi form a network of threads, called the mycelium (the threads are called hyphae), that runs between different plants. To help explain, this scenario will refer to forest trees.

The symbiotic relationship between some fungi, like the arbuscular mycorrhizal, and the plants they're connected to, is inspiring. It's an apt demonstration of interspecies cooperation for mutual benefit. The extensive network of fungi mycelium has access to water and nutrients usually unavailable to the roots. But because of the symbiotic relationship, water and nutrients are brought to the plant. These are absorbed by the tree and taken to the leaves. The leaves convert the water and carbon dioxide into dextrose through photosynthesis using the sun's energy. The excess dextrose and carbon dioxide are channeled to the roots, where the mycelia benefit. This is essential as the fungi are unable to produce their own dextrose. This process is called mycorrhiza.

Recent studies[7] show that there could be multiple mycorrhiza species around one tree, forming an information network with other trees. Stronger trees, called anchor trees, are able to benefit smaller trees by supplying them with nutrients through the network. DNA tests have shown that a single anchor tree (the tallest one that gets the most light) can be connected to as many as 47 benefactor trees – all through the mycorrhiza.

AM Fungi

Due to their ability to colonize most crop plants, arbuscular mycorrhizal (AM) fungi are the most essential mycorrhizae in agricultural ecosystems. AM fungi are obligate symbionts (roughly translated as compulsive coworkers) and must associate with plant roots to survive. As per the example above, AM, using their network of hyphae, act as an extension of a plant's root system, which provides the plant with access to immobile nutrients. While plant root hairs extend a mere fraction of an inch into the soil, the mycorrhiza's hyphae can extend up to an additional 6 inches from the roots. Mycorrhizae and crop plants are linked beneficially. Mycorrhizae are still responsible

---

7   *https://www.youtube.com/watch?v=7kHZ0a_6TxY*

for most phosphorus uptake, even if there is no growth enhancement, which is rarely the case. Additionally, mycorrhizae have been linked to improved disease resistance, drought tolerance, and soil structure for plants.

Tillage and phosphorus fertilizer applications impede the development of mycorrhizae, but responsible farming practices can bolster localized populations. Legume crops have a strong partnership with AM and are often used as a cover crop to boost maize crops. Initially, it was believed that AM secured nitrogen for subsequent crops. Still, there's growing evidence that AM effectively accesses immobile phosphorus for plants, boosting their health and productivity.

AM FUNGI INOCULUM

It's beyond the scope of this book to delve into the production of AM inoculum. The reference is aimed at piquing the reader's interest in the power of the microbial world in affecting plant growth. Composting is at the cusp of providing the world with the arsenal to better use the pedosphere. I believe we only know enough to be intrigued. The best is yet to come.

For those interested in exploring more regarding the production of AM inoculum, the best accessible information is on the Rodale Institute's website.

EFFECTIVE MICROORGANISMS

Does everyone imagine scenarios of living in a lawless country, or is it just a Tony thing? Imagine a state where the innocent are subject to persecution and where criminals rule. Imagine seeking help from a police officer, only to be accused of a crime you didn't commit. Living in a state where the gatekeepers of justice are the lawbreakers must be horrible. My grandfather had a quote: "The only thing necessary for evil to triumph is for good men to do nothing." But what if there are no good men, or very few of them?

Think of your soil as a state. In the absence of good organisms, harmful organisms rule (such as nematodes). These are organisms (though not technically microorganisms), some of which are responsible for plant diseases.

Aside: Please note that only a tiny segment of the nematode population creates havoc. Nematodes are important grazers in soil biota, enhancing soil quality in four ways:

- *Regulating soil biota populations*
- *Mineralizing nutrients into plant-available forms (by culling microorganisms)*
- *Acting as a food source for other predators*
- *Consuming disease-causing organisms*

If their population is too high, they consume mycorrhizal fungi, an essential symbiotic benefactor of many plants. Fortunately there are predator nematodes (cannibals) that control the nematode population.

The principle of a dominant culture implies a group of people who set the tone for the rest of the population. These are those whose values and ways of behaving are imposed on a subordinate culture or cultures through religion, education, and economic or political power. Activists are those from a sub-culture who challenge the dominant culture's norms. Passivists are the conformists, being inert, suffering acceptance, or not resisting wrong.

In the world of microorganisms, there are many passivists. Whatever the dominant culture of the soil biota, they function within the confines of that system, often as prey. As gardeners, we can influence the dominant culture within the soil biota by adding "good cops," also called effective microorganisms. By boosting the population of effective microorganisms (EM®), we can stabilize the environment to benefit the soil and the plants.

EM was developed by Professor Teruo Higa[8] in 1982. Dr. Teruo Higa is a professor emeritus at the University of the Ryukyus in Okinawa, Japan. He is also the director at the International EM Technology Center of Meio University in Okinawa. In the 1970s, Dr. Higa postulated the theory of soil biota dominant culture, just in different words. He argued that if the soil can be populated with a combination of solid and effective microorganisms, the ecosystem would follow suit and become balanced for the benefit of that environment.

---

8   *https://emrojapan.com/dr-higa*

EM capitalizes on synergistic effects of combining beneficial microorganisms, specifically lactic acid bacteria, yeast, and phototrophic bacteria. In essence, EM activates microorganisms native to the soil and water and maximizes their natural power. The core ingredients of EM are photosynthetic bacteria (Rhodopseudomonas spp.), lactic acid bacteria (Lactobacillus spp.), and yeasts (Saccharomyces spp.). While we'll consider each culture separately, it's important to note that the strength of EM is based on the synergistic effect of the sum of all ingredients. The definition of synergy is *when the combined effect is greater than the sum of their separate effects.*

- The **photosynthetic bacteria** are unique in that they are self-sustaining, independent microorganisms. Harvesting energy from the sun and soil heat, they convert root exudates, organic fraction, and ammonia into building cells (amino acids, nucleic acids, and sugars).

- The **lactic acid bacteria** produce lactic acid from carbohydrates. Lactic acid is a sterilizing agent that keeps nematode populations in check and protects plants from diseases they cause. It has also been shown that lactic acid bacteria break cellulolytic and lignified organic materials down.

- Cell and root division is encouraged by **yeast's** production of hormones and enzymes. The photosynthetic bacteria and plant roots secrete amino acids and sugars used by the lactic acid bacteria to produce growth factors. Therefore, we can deduce that EM's diverse species of organisms harmonize with each other and the soil ecosystem's plant roots to benefit both parties. Soil containing and dominated by these beneficial microorganisms would produce exceptional plant growth.

Plants can be protected from soil-related diseases caused by pathogenic microorganisms and parasites if the soil biota is in good health. Pathogenic and beneficial microorganisms can coexist productively in the soil, provided there are sufficient "good cops." The difference between healthy and *dead* soil is the dominance of beneficial microorganisms. Fermenting the organic fraction of soil results in humus rich in nutrients and is active in releasing hormones that aid plant growth. Their job is to provide plants with the necessary hormones, nutrients, and minerals via the root system. In addition, they aid in retaining nutrients and moisture by creating aggregates.

Many microorganisms live in decomposed organic materials. When introduced to the soil, some of these organisms have beneficial effects. Naturally occurring soil organisms may eventually displace or eliminate these introduced species. The converse is also true – introduced effective microorganisms can displace or eliminate local microbial populations. EM is a rich concentration of beneficial synergistic microorganisms able to restructure the soil biota for good.

Effective Microorganisms Benefits

Compost or compost tea's beneficial effects on microorganisms can be short-lived, exposing crop plants to soil-dominant conditions. EM mixtures are also exposed to the same soil conditions as other soil treatment processes on application. On the other hand, effective microorganisms have a significant advantage over organic amendments in that beneficial microorganisms are introduced in more significant numbers and in optimally balanced populations. As a result, they would remain in the soil environment for a much more extended period, long enough to have the desired effects.

The use of beneficial microorganisms in agricultural soil has been shown to reduce soil-borne pathogens, promote organic decomposition, and increase the availability of mineral nutrients and other essential organic compounds to plants. EM also enhances the activities of beneficial indigenous microorganisms such as mycorrhizae, which fix atmospheric nitrogen as an alternative to chemical fertilizers and pesticides. Crop growth, flowering, fruit development, and ripening are all aided by increased soil fertility, a product of EM.

Soil-associated microbiological diseases can be reduced by introducing a population of effective microorganisms (EM). The rotation effect occurs when beneficial organisms are regenerated and pathogenic bacteria are eliminated through the inoculation of EM. Competition for resources between soil-borne pathogens and beneficial microbes introduced via EM results in disease suppression. Increased inoculation of effective microorganisms will deplete soil resources, causing pathogenic microorganisms to suffer from starvation as a result.

Rhodopseudomonas species, Lactobacillus species, and yeast species are the three mainstays of EM. Photosynthetic bacteria (Rhodopseudomanas spp.) convert organic fraction, root exudates, and ammonia into amino acids, nucleic acids, and sugars using solar and soil heat energy. Many beneficial microorganisms can grow and thrive in the soil with the help of these nutrients, which can also be taken up by plants directly. The AM fungi live in association with rhizobium and azotobacter, which increase the capacity of plants to fix nitrogen.

Lactic acid bacteria use the sugars and carbohydrates produced by the photosynthetic bacteria and yeasts to create lactic acid. Lactic acid is a sterilizing agent that keeps nematode populations in check and protects plants from diseases they cause. The breakdown of decay-resistant cellulose and lignin is also aided by lactic acid bacteria in EM.

Plant cell and root division are aided by EM yeast-produced hormones and enzymes. The lactic acid bacteria grow using the sugars and amino acids secreted by the photosynthetic bacteria and plant roots. The synergy between the different EM cultures becomes evident. This is truly a symphony of mutually beneficial relationships between plants and the soil biota, each benefiting the other and creating a harmonious, healthy whole.

Using EM

In **Chapter 7 – Anaerobic Composting,** I review Bokashi composting, a system that depends on effective microorganisms. EM is supplied in liquid form commercially. Even though the product is registered and patented, it appears that there is scant regard for Professor Higa's intellectual property. I'm pretty sure that the original product is superior to the rip-offs. That said, the principles are fast becoming broadly studied, and the honorable Dr. Higa is an avid defender of non-competitiveness, a reflection of the dominant culture in Japan.

The liquid form is a concentration of effective microorganisms discussed above. For general use, the concentration is generally diluted or dispersed on a carrier bulking agent, like bran or rice hulls.

Here I review the section in Chapter 7 describing how to make the bulking agent that can be used in your compost piles, in Bokashi composting, or as a medium for vermicomposting.

Helpful Conversions
- One gallon is equal to 19 cups (19.2152 exactly)
- One gallon of water weighs 8.345 pounds

Ingredients and Tools
- 12.5-pounds of wheat bran (or rice hulls)
- One cup of Bokashi EM-1® (NOT EMA – EMA is not a concentrate EM)
- One cup of molasses (or freshly squeezed fruit juice. Do not use fruit juices with preservatives)

- 60 fl. oz. of warm water (120 degrees Fahrenheit) – preferably unchlorinated or dechlorinated
- Large mixing container (not washed in antibacterial detergent – wiped, instead, with diluted EM-1®)
- A potato masher
- A plastic sheet big enough to cover the container top. While many suggest using a refuse sack, don't use antibacterial versions)

EM-1® Inoculum Bran Recipe

Step 1

Add the wheat bran or rice hulls to the mixing bowl. If you buy wheat bran in bulk, it ought to cost you just over 50c per pound if bought in bulk - rice hulls are a bit more expensive. Wheat bran for worm farms is also a suitable alternative. Your EM-1® inoculated bran is also ideal for vermicomposting bedding. Because we want maximum surface area, the finer, the better. The microorganisms in EM-1® inoculated bran are anaerobic, so we don't have concerns about compaction.

Step 2

Mix the Molasses, EM-1®, and water. Your water is one-quarter of the weight of your wheat bran (12.5 divided by 4 = 3.125 pounds of water) – which is 60 fluid ounces or just more than 7 cups. Your EM-1® is one-seventh of the water added. Remember, warm water (not hot) stimulates your effective microorganism's activity and makes it easier to dissolve the molasses (or treacle).

Step 3

Add your fluids to the dry ingredients. Thoroughly mix your water mixture in with the wheat bran, ensuring that there are no dry pockets. The bran (or rice hulls) are hydrophobic (repel water), so work through the batch systematically. If your bran stock is super dry, add additional water a little at a time. Take care to not let your bran mix get too wet – the purpose of the water is to be a carrier of the effective microorganisms. You want the batch to be damp - not wet and not dry.

Step 4

Remove as much air as you can. Use the potato masher to press your mix to the bottom of your bucket, removing as much air as you can. Use your plastic sheet to isolate your mix from oxygen – tucking the sheet in around the edges. The effective microorganisms in EM-1® do best in anaerobic conditions. Store the EM-1® inoculated bran in an air-free bag if you have a vacuum pump.

Step 5

Store in an airtight container for a month at moderate temperatures out of direct sunlight. It is best to leave the newly manufactured batch of inoculum untouched for a minimum of two weeks before use. The longer it stays in anaerobic conditions, the more your effective microorganisms get an opportunity to grow and multiply. As they consume the molasses, they will run out of carbohydrates, at which point they will become dormant. When the color turns darker and the smell sweet-and-sour, fermentation is completed.

Step 6 (optional)

As a sixth step, you can choose to dry the EM-1® bran inoculum and store it for up to 2-years. You can do this by spreading the fully inoculated mixture on a tarp in the shade to dry it out.

If the weather doesn't permit this, you can dry it in batches in an oven with the door open and the temperature set to as low as possible. You do not want to heat your EM-1® bran higher than 120-degrees Fahrenheit.

This process is unnecessary if your batch will be used within 3-months or if you particularly need a damp EM-1® inoculated bran (like bedding for your worms). Either way, you now have a supply of homemade EM-1® bran inoculum to use in your Bokashi bin, vermicomposting bin, composting pile, or garden. The dry version is an excellent way to control moisture when adding food scraps to either your Bokashi bin, compost pile, or worm farm. Also, use the EM-1® inoculated bran to cover food scraps to prevent them from attracting pests.

SUMMARY OF OTHER COMPOSTING METHODS

Composting is essentially manipulating soil biota diversity by cultivating microorganisms using organic matter. There are several methods of achieving this goal, each with its pros and cons. It would be an error on my part to define the best process. However, I'm biased towards traditional aerobic composting, enhanced by vermicomposting. In the end, the choice is influenced by several factors, including the availability of materials, space, time, and the intended application.

There is no right way, and each method and inoculate has merit. The intention is to expose you to the whole general scope of composting. I use the word *"general"* because the science is more complex, and effective composting requires knowing your actual soil biota and the diversity and population of your compost. This is only possible with a microscope and the knowledge of its practical use. Composting is an exciting field and is fast becoming a dedicated science and economic participant.

In **Chapter 10 – Composting Use**, we will review the breadth of composting and inocula applications. The next chapter reviews the vessels and structures we can use for the different composting methods.

9. COMPOSTING VESSELS

This chapter reviews 10 home composting vessel designs available in the public domain[9], initially commissioned by the former California Integrated Waste Management Board and now distributed by the Central Vermont Solid Waste Management District.

OPEN PILE

HARDWARE CLOTH BIN

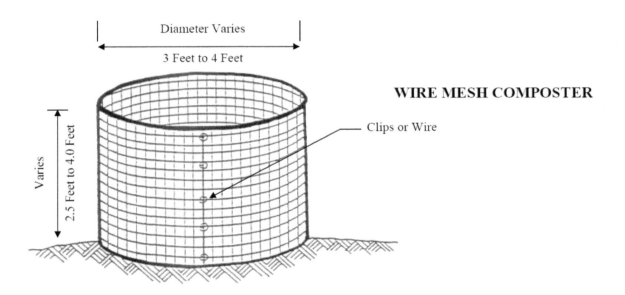

Hardware cloth, for the uninformed, is not cloth as the name may suggest but is a welded mesh manufactured from galvanized steel wire. A hardware cloth bin is an easy-to-build and inexpensive way to have a structured compost pile. This bin doesn't require posts, is easy to move to any location, and allows ample air to pass through. It is also easy to cover the mesh with a tarp if weather conditions affect your batch. This simple structure is the vessel of choice for many an astute gardener.

---

9   *http://www.cvswmd.org/uploads/6/1/2/6/6126179/variety_of_bin_plans.pdf*

What you need to make a hardware cloth composting bin

Tools
- Gloves
- Safety goggles
- Stanley knife

Materials
All you need is a length of 0.5-inch-grid hardware cloth, 3 or 4 feet wide. Your end product will stand a minimum of 3 feet high with a diameter of 3 feet. The formula to determine a circumference is:

$$C = 2\pi r$$

$$C = 2 \times 3.1416 \times 1.5$$

The circumference of a 3-foot-wide circle is approximately 9.5 feet. Add 6 inches for the overlap, and you need a 10 foot length of hardware cloth for your cylindrical composting bin.

- A 10-foot-long, 3-foot-wide piece of hardware cloth. Purchasing additional length will allow you to create a sieving frame in addition to the compost bin
- Cable or zip ties
- A 9.5 foot length of ½ inch diameter PVC irrigation pipe (optional)

Method
- Using the hardware cloth, create a free-standing cylinder 3 feet tall and with a diameter of 3 feet.
- Use the cable ties to fix the overlapping 6 inches together.
- Optional protection: Slit the irrigation pipe from end-to-end and use it to cover the top of the hardware cloth cylinder to prevent injury from protruding wire edges.

PALLET BAYS COMPOSTING UNITS

Compost is the blood in the veins of any garden and supports and feeds all microbial life and improves soil health. It helps with water retention, pH control, soil structure, and erosion. Personally, this is my favorite method, and as can be seen in my YouTube video, this is what I use.

What you need to make a three-bay pallet compost bin system

Tools
- Gloves
- Two-direction power drill with Torx/Star screwdriver fitting
- A large set square (alternatively use the Pythagoras theorem)
- A spade to level the surface (if required)
- An upholstery staple gun with staples
- Safety goggles

Materials
- Six pallets. Look for 36x36-inch pallets. Those made of recycled wood will be suitable as the whole structure will be covered with weed barrier landscape fabric
- About 30 #14 x 6 inch Construction Lag Screws, coated, and with Torx/Star washer heads

- A roll of heavy-duty weed barrier landscape fabric. Preferably black polypropylene
- A piece of carpet

Method

The first thing you need to consider is where you're going to place your compost. Ideally, you don't want to place it in full sun, nor do you want to place it underneath the trees. If you place it too close to trees, the runoff of the compost can affect the root system. However, there is always a caveat to these two rules. You really need to place that compost where you're going to use it.

So let's get to building a compost bin from pallets.

The first thing you need to do is create a level area where we will build our pallet compost bin.

- Then, start by standing two of the pallets to create a corner. Ensure that both pallets have the tops facing into the compost bin and screw these together through the supporting blocks of the pallet with six-inch screws.

- Once this has been done on all three supporting blocks, we need to square up this corner before adding the third sidewall. If you skip this step, the front will not fit in, and the structure might be unstable.

- Lift the third wall and screw this as we did the previous sides. We now have a bay built and in place.

- We can now make this stronger if we desire by capping the top surface of the pallets with extra planks of timber, especially at the corners. This will give the top a solid surface and also help strengthen the compost bin.

- Before we worry about the front of this compost bin, we need to wrap it in heavy-duty weed barrier landscape fabric. Simply start on the sides and staple the covering into place. Work around the entire compost bin and then fold and cut the top and staple it down.

- The front is created by screwing two pieces the height of the compost bin in the middle of the blocks. This creates the space to form part of the slot where the front doors slide in from the top.

- Screw onto each of these a flat plank that will create a slot. And the front is ready to receive its doors.

- The doors are straightforward to make. Cut a number of 2x4 planks the length of the gap between two slots on either side of the compost bin. Allow about a 1 inch gap for the front to slide easily.

- I suggest making the front in two sections, as seen on my YouTube video, to be removed in sections.

- All you need now is to cut a piece of plastic to cover the bin when it's filled and a piece of carpet to go over the top of that.

- When selecting your pallets, you want to look for the HT symbol. That means that these pallets have been heat-treated only, and they haven't been impregnated with chemicals that could leach into your garden. The blue and red pallets that you get, typically on construction sites and industrial parks, have all been treated with chemicals and should be avoided.

So there we have it, a good-sized compost bin that will take about a ton of compost. This is something that you can stick in your garden, and it's not going to look unsightly. It's going to help you get the best compost you possibly can, which is full of nutrients.

Ideally, you want three of these in a row to make it easy to turn and still have space for keeping fresh material aside from the bin in the thermophilic phase of composting.

CINDER BLOCK COMPOST BIN

The standard size of a cinder block is 15.625 inches long and 7.625 inches high and wide. Stacking three cinder blocks in a row and overlapping one creates an inner diameter of 39.25 inches, the ideal size for a bin. Five layers will give you a height of just over 38 inches.

What you need to make a cinder block composting bin

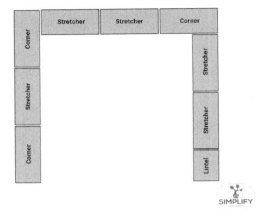

Cinder Block Composting Bin

Tools
- Spade
- Spirit level
- Gloves

Materials
For a neat finish, each *layer* requires:
- Five stretcher cinder blocks (open-ended on both sides)
- Three corner cinder blocks (edged on one side)
- One beam or lintel block (half, edged on one side)

The full materials list:
- 25 stretcher cinder blocks
- 15 corner cinder blocks
- Five beam or lintel cinder blocks

Method

- Ensure the base is level by using a spirit level. You might need to rework the base until you have a four-foot square area that is perfectly flat.
- Stack your first layer as indicated. The ½-size capping stone at the end must have a flat edge outward.
- Each layer is a mirror image of the previous layer, overlapping the block below halfway.

There are several advantages to a cinder block bin, including its ease to build, presentability, and perfect size for composting. The importance of starting on a level base cannot be overstated. If you decide to add a front to your bin, I suggest you drive a 2x2 stake into the ground at each of the front ends, on which you can attach a 2x4 to create a slot. I would use three boards the width of the bin and a foot high for the front closure. Slide the boards from the top to close the front in sections, adding the composting matter as it becomes available in the proper carbon to nitrogen ratios.

COMPOST TUMBLER

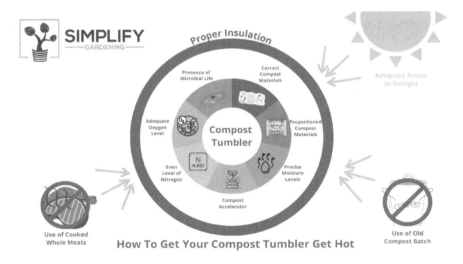

How To Get Your Compost Tumbler Get Hot

On my website[10], I have several articles on the use of compost tumblers. If your backyard is relatively small, you might be facing challenges with creating compost. Creating compost the traditional way requires some space and effort. However, using a barrel offers a way to simplify the turning process with some success. But tumblers can be ineffective for several reasons:

- The most common challenge is that the batch doesn't mix when turned. Instead, you can end up with a revolving mass that is hot on the inside, with limited decomposition on the outside.

- Access to the tumbler for turning intervention is not always easy.

10   *https://simplifygardening.com/?s=tumbler*

- Too frequent turning can interrupt the thermophilic phase. Ideally, you want higher temperatures for three days to destroy pathogens and weed seeds. Frequent turning without measuring temperatures can frustrate the process.

While these innovations can seem like a solution to make composting more manageable and faster, the tumbler process can become ineffective if proper care is not taken. On the positive side, tumblers are a space-saver and can work if used appropriately.

- Ensure you have a tumbler bin that is darker and well insulated to attract more heat.

- Ensure that your batch has the correct moisture content. Tumblers get hot, resulting in high evaporation. On the other hand, a batch that is too wet will soon become anaerobic, causing putrefaction and foul odors.

- Ensure a proper C:N ratio of 30:1 from the start. This is a single-batch process, and adding additional material over time will be counterproductive.

- Make sure that the added material has been shredded. Porosity is less essential with tumblers, as the turning process is active, but shredded material cascades with each tumbler revolution, ensuring a better mixing. The thermophilic higher temperatures may cause parts of the batch to clump, so after each turn (every five to six days), make sure that there are no big clumps. There may be smaller clumps as the bacteria secrete binding agents.

STYROFOAM WORM BIN

Few composting options can produce a higher quality compost than red wiggler worms, kitchen scraps, and aerobic compost. Vermicomposting can reduce aerobic compost, inoculated Bokashi bran, and vegetable scraps to worm casting equivalent to a 3:3:3 NPK ratio fertilizer with the added benefit of retaining the microorganisms needed for soil health.

Styrofoam is the most cost-effective formable insulation material and is commonly used in the fish industry, where the cold-chain needs to be preserved. Unfortunately, polystyrene is highly resistant to degradation (except photodegradation) and can last up to 800 years in a landfill where it's not exposed to sunlight.

If you can save a bin from the trash, use it to make a worm bin. I realize it's banned in Portland, OR, Orange County, CA, and probably more counties.

Preparing a Container
- Using the suggested 18x36 inch Styrofoam container (minimum 8 inches deep, ideally 12 to 16 inches), use a serrated knife to cut a half-inch slot about an inch-and-a-half from the bottom on the narrow (18 inch) sides.

- The slot should provide the worms with sufficient aeration and should be about 8 to 12 inches long – parallel to the base.

- Create a 6 inch square slot in the center of the lid as well.

- Cover any holes in the bin with a non-metallic fly-screen (geotextile material). You can attach rust-proof fine netting on the inside using a glue gun. Some glues react with polystyrene, but a glue gun works well. You only need to attach it at the corners as the weight of the bedding will prevent gaps from forming at the edges. The netting must be fine enough to prevent worms from escaping yet permeable enough for unrestricted airflow. Metallic netting will deteriorate in wet and acidic environments.

- While some will advise you to create holes at the bottom for drainage, I will show you how to avoid leachate forming so holes are not needed.

- Do not use a transparent bin – it allows too much light in. Avoid direct sunlight if you use a black bin as the bin will overheat, killing your worms.

CONCLUSION TO COMPOSTING VESSELS

To the creativity of humans, there is no end. For aerobic composting, you need a space that, minimally, will keep a cubic yard of material together. I have seen compost bins that are innovative, beautiful, and obviously effectively functional. But all the creativity in the world cannot replace you, the gardener. The success of any composting vessel depends on the gardener's skills. May the microorganisms be with you as you create your vessel for magic.

10. USING COMPOST IN YOUR GARDEN

The proof of the pudding is in the eating. The proof of your effort, care, and dedication are in the benefits the compost offers your garden. While we can all wax lyrical about the techniques used and the organisms in our compost, the impact of its application is what matters. That said, nature has its own timing. Earlier in the book, I reference a compacted construction site where compost was added to the surface. It took four years for that soil to recover. Similar cases have been reported for mining sites and abused soil – it takes a while, but it works.

AERATED COMPOST

ENSURING YOUR COMPOST IS CURED

Only use cured, stable aerobic compost in your garden. Uncured compost is unstable and leaches nitrogen from your soil to decompose the remaining carbon. In the process, it temporarily destabilizes the soil biota. Rather than boosting your soil's capacity, uncured compost temporarily has the opposite effect. Stabilized compost is identifiable by:

- Its effect on seed germination speeds. Uncured aerobic compost retards the germination of seeds. A simple comparative test between seeds watered by compost extract and unchlorinated water, respectively, can quickly show if your compost is stable or not.

- The petrichor smell, which is from geosmin, an actinomycete secretion. It is also the triple-bonded oxygen molecule of ozone (O3). The Merriam-Webster dictionary describes it as *"a distinctive, earthy, usually pleasant odor that is associated with rainfall, especially when following a warm, dry period."*

- A dark brown color, similar to that of a 70% dark chocolate – not caramel and not black.

- A crumbliness, like a fresh scone. Over-composting at excessive temperatures will result in a powdery mass.

- There are no signs of thermal activity because fully cured compost no longer heats up.

Please note that there's a difference between cured and old compost. Old compost has dried out and has lost some of its value to evaporation and possible leaching. Ideally, you want to incorporate your compost into the soil within six months of making it. It requires two months maximum to cure – even less if your process was managed. Regular turning towards the end of the manufacturing process will see incrementally receding temperature peaks. The batch is stable when it no longer heats up when turned.

COMPOST GRADING

To improve the serviceability of your stable aerated compost, you may consider first grading it. If you're planning on using it on your lawns, then first sieve it through a ¼-inch mesh. For your garden, you may up that size to half an inch. Sieving also removes the harder to decompose bits like thicker branch pieces. These pieces can be reincorporated into your next batch of compost for their final journey towards decomposition.

Creating a sieve can be a fun project. All you need is three or four sections of two-by-four planks to form a frame that will fit over a garden wagon or wheelbarrow. Cover the frame with hardware mesh of the required size and sieve the compost for direct application onto or into your beds or lawn.

Winter is unsuitable for applying compost, but the other seasons are all great. If you're planning on an annual garden refresher event, fall is a great time to add volumes of compost – after the first frosts but before the big freeze.

Spreading compost above ground is a highly viable option to benefit your soil without disturbing the established soil biota. Studies have shown that construction sites where the soil is severely compacted benefit from unincorporated compost layers (like the forests do). Just remember to occasionally wet the compost to prevent it from drying out. Take note that the soil biota will take some time to stabilize when compost is added to the soil. It's advisable to wait for a couple of weeks after adding compost before planting in beds. Summer applications can be directly on the plants or adjacent to the plants. Either way, the plant

roots will attract the microorganisms, which will attract their predators to release the nutrients held in their bodies – a beautiful symphony of purpose and life.

Compost Yields

I advise that you keep your compost at 50% moisture throughout until used (within six months of making it). Too moist will cause anaerobic conditions, and humidity levels below 15% will cause your microorganisms to die.

- A full cubic-yard-sized bin (the size of a standard composting bin) will produce just over 12 cubic feet of compost weighing about 150 pounds – enough to cover 150 square feet of soil an inch deep

- Compost weighs approximately 12.5 pounds per cubic foot (specific gravity 0.2)

- A spread of 0.5 inches thick will cover 300 sq. ft. from a single composted pile of 3 cubic foot (1 cubic yard)

- An application of 0.5 inches of aerobic compost across the garden bed is adequate for annual maintenance regimes

AEROBIC COMPOST USE

Annual flower and vegetable beds

Timing
The best time to apply compost on vegetable patches and garden beds is either side of winter – late fall or early spring. The winter months may be dormant or partially active, depending on your region's climate. Spring, however, conjures up images of bloom and vitality. Just remember that you need a gap between committing aerated compost to the soil and planting – about two weeks.

Healthy Beds
Spread the bed with a layer of compost about an inch thick. Lightly incorporate in the top three inches of soil – if at all. You want to minimize disturbing the present soil biota. Whatever you add will be incorporated into the bed. Amid all this serious stuff, permit me to tell you a joke. Each morning, this couple woke up and noticed that, during the night, somebody had added compost to their yard. The plot thickens.

Remedial Applications
If the bed hasn't had compost for several years, you'll be required to actively populate the soil with a healthy soil biota. Spread the bed with a layer of compost about 3 inches thick. Incorporate by turning it into the soil to a depth of about 4 to 6 inches.

Mulching
Add compost mulching during summer months, covering the bed with an additional inch of compost or mulch. Aerobic compost mulching has the following benefits:

- Mulch is effective in reducing evaporation from the soil surface
- Mulch limits weed seed germination. Word of advice: If your beds produce weeds after applying compost, there could be three reasons:
  1. Your aerobic thermophilic phases weren't hot enough.
  2. Your compost got contaminated with weed seeds during the curing process.
  3. The soil has weed seeds, and your compost has a small fungi population. Higher fungi populations limit weed seed germination. Using fish hydrolysis as food, you could remedy the situation with active aerobic compost tea (AACT).
- Mulch acts as an insulator, protecting plants from temperature extremes
- Mulch interrupts the flow of water on sloped areas, preventing erosion

- Mulch reduces soil compaction caused by heavy rain
- Aerobic compost mulch activates the development of a diverse soil biota necessary for healthy soil
- Aerobic compost mulch adds valuable nutrients to your soil close to plants

Perennials

Perennials are a game-changer in preserving the soil's vitality. Millions are being invested in finding perennial food crops to replace maize and wheat, both annual crops that require disruption of the soil biota. Only 15% of the total calories consumed are produced by perennial food plants.

One inch of compost or leaf mold can often eliminate the need for additional fertilization in your garden. You can avoid overfertilization by learning about each plant's requirements and keeping an eye on its leaf color and growth pattern.

Most perennials will benefit from a topdressing of 1 to 2 inches of compost over their beds. Some perennials are naturally heavy feeders. In addition to a spring feeding, plants such as daylilies, peonies, mums (Chrysanthemum), and tall phlox benefit from a second feeding in the summer. If you cut your perennials back to allow new foliage and blooms to shoot, use compost tea for summer feeding to get the best results. This includes delphiniums, daisies, and lungworts.

When planting perennials, especially food plants like strawberries, raspberries, rhubarb, and asparagus, dig a hole or trench 8 inches wide and about 18 inches deep and fill it with compost. Folding compost into established perennial beds is not advised as you're likely to injure the roots. Instead, use compost tea to reach deeper, or cover with an inch or inch-and-a-half top dressing.

Trees and Shrubs

Whether a person, plant, or worm – relocation is traumatic. You want to optimize initial establishment but don't want to promote roots remaining bound. If you fill the hole with compost, trees will be reluctant to spread their roots, and newly introduced tree or shrub roots will have no need to reach out into the harder surrounding soil. Following a maximum gain and least resistance route, roots will grow in a circle and impede the tree's (or shrub's) growth. Eventually, the tree will strangle itself.

If, however, you wet the bottom and sides of the hole with freshly made active aerobic compost tea (AACT), the surrounding soil will become a fertile environment for the roots to explore. It will encourage their growth and spread, extending a healthy soil biota in the process. Remember to water the newly planted tree to a radius wider than the initial hole.

FOR ESTABLISHED TREES AND SHRUBS

If your grass is not flourishing under trees, remove it up to the plant's dripline. This is the imaginary circle around your tree where most branches, or the canopy, ends and most of the rain drips from. Remove any grass, exposing bare soil to cover with about an inch-thick layer of compost. Work this into the soil to a depth of about 3 inches. You don't want to damage the roots but stimulate a healthy soil biome. Cover the composted area with leaf mold (about 3 inches) to improve the compost's fungi population, insulation, water retention, and weed control. Leaf mold also creates a pleasant surface to walk on. Trees and shrubs prefer a higher fungi-to-bacteria ratio.

If you have a healthy lawn mix of shade-tolerant grasses already established, see below.

Lawns

Grass Clippings

There are benefits to leaving clippings on the lawn rather than composting them. If, however, your lawn is infected, then aerobic composting done correctly is the best way to benefit from the loss. Your lawn thrives on nitrogen which is abundantly present in lawn clippings. While many may think that grass clipping contributes to thatch formation, the truth is that over-fertilization is the culprit.

Before we proceed, consider the following facts:

- Adding yard waste, such as leaves, grass clippings, and branches, to your trash has been banned nationally since March 1995
- Yard waste accounts for approximately one-fifth of all waste material
- Clippings left on the lawn could contribute as much as a quarter of your lawn's total fertilizer needs
- Because clippings contain as much as 80% to 85% water, they decompose quickly
- Not having to bag clippings can reduce the average mowing time by as much as 50%

When fully considered, grass clippings make up a surprisingly large portion of waste – approximately 300 to 400 pounds of grass clippings per 1,000 square feet annually or, put differently, 6.5 tons per acre each year. Reusing this valuable resource through grasscycling is the solution.

The correct guideline for lawn mowing is not to remove more than the top third of the leaf. Generally, the best length of a lawn is between 2.5 and 4 inches, depending on the grass cultivar. If you're creating a putting green in your back yard with some Bermuda Grass or Bent Grass, you want it low. But generally, you should cut your grass before it reaches 4 inches long, maximally removing the top inch.

The shorter your clippings, the less impact they have on your mowed surface. You may need to acquire a retrofit kit, and your local mower dealer can help you select a suitable one. Mulching mowers make grasscycling easy by cutting grass blades into small pieces and forcing them into the soil. Of course, an electric mulching mower will reduce air pollution.

If your lawn has fungal growth, do not leave the clippings on the lawn. Instead, use the clippings as part of your compost heap. The temperatures generated by the composting process will break any organisms down. Fungal infections will present as white tips on the end of the grass blade.

Lawn Dressing

A healthy lawn is an asset and a testimony to the gardener's proficiency as a groundskeeper. Composting can add a whole new dimension to your lawn growing. We know that a healthy soil biota boosts aggregates' formation and increases nutrient availability and moisture retention. With an improved soil structure (aggregates), the roots can grow deeper, giving the plant better access to water and nutrients. Plants with deep root structures are more drought tolerant.

You want fine-grained compost that can get down to the roots for lawn composting. So, two things need to be done before adding the compost – providing access to the roots and sieving your compost. The latter is described in the intro to this chapter. To get the compost to the roots, you need to use an aerator – a spiked roller. If you don't have one, a garden fork works just as well but burns more calories.

Spread the compost about a quarter-inch thick across the surface – about 2 pounds per square yard. Using a rubber lawn rake, rake the compost to increase the amount going into the aeration holes. Once done, water thoroughly – about an inch of water across the surface. To measure an inch, place a couple of 1-inch-deep empty tuna cans on the lawn – when they're full, you've watered an inch.

If your lawn has some bald patches, use a spade to cut 6 inches deep around the edges of the patch. Then cover with about 2 inches of compost, work it in to a depth of 6 inches all the way to the cut circumference. Level off, scatter some grass seeds over, and water thoroughly. If there are toxins in the soil, the microorganisms will neutralize them.

New Lawns

When planting a lawn, one of the first considerations is the layout – shade presence, soil type, soil acidity, drainage, and other plants. As you will be planting your new lawn from grass seed, preparing a seedbed of soil free of weeds, clods and stones is a starting point. Water the area and allow it to stand for a week to give weed seeds time to germinate. This will give you a chance to pull them out before they seed and before you compost, plant your seeds, or lay your sod. Repeat the process if there are a lot of weeds – culling them from a virgin bed is much easier than from a lawn. Do not use any herbicides, pesticides, or chemical fertilizers.

Now bring the biology back into the soil. Spread a 3 inch layer of aerated comport across the whole surface and incorporate it into the top 8 inches of the soil – where your future pristine lawn's roots will be. You can roll your seedbed, ensuring it is as level as practically possible. This extra effort is worth the sense of satisfaction and achievement you'll experience for years to come. Wait for at least two weeks before sowing the seed or laying the sod. Keep the area damp during all this time.

There are approximately 14 different grass types to choose from. Here is a quick summary for your convenience:

WARM-SEASON GRASSES
- Bermuda Grass
- Centipede Grass
- St Augustine Grass
- Zoysia Grass
- Bahia Grass
- Buffalo Grass
- Seashore Paspalum

- Bent Grass
- Dichondra Repens

COOL-SEASON GRASSES
- Kentucky Bluegrass
- Perennial Ryegrass
- Fine Fescue
- Tall Fescues
- Creeping Bent Grass

Water the lawn regularly to keep the top inch of soil consistently moist, critical for seed germination. Reduce watering once the grass begins to grow to allow the roots to establish.

Container Plants

When creating a potting mix, avoid adding more than a third of compost by volume to the mix. The balance of the mix could be an equal part of coconut coir and vermiculite. This will provide you with a healthy environment that can hold water (coconut coir), ensure ample aeration (vermiculite), and provide your plant with access to the proper nutrients at the right time (compost). Ensure that you use mature compost as uncured compost may contain latent phytotoxins that could damage your plant.

COMPOST TEA

NON-AERATED COMPOST EXTRACT AND ACTIVELY AERATED COMPOST TEA

You may have always thought, as I did, that straining water through compost using a bag produces compost tea. Well, it is and it isn't. Straining water through compost is an effective way of extracting humic acid from compost. Humic acid is a type of magic wand for the interaction of cation and anions. It is a game-changer for promoting a healthier soil structure and nutrient availability (essential primary nutrients). Sound like a microorganism? It's actually a microorganisms' best friend. Filling a stocking with compost and straining it in water is a great way to get the benefits of compost into a liquid form that can access roots without disturbing the soil biota.

Actively aerated compost tea (AACT) is a very different magic. During the process, we are essentially ensuring our microorganism friends are kept invigorated with a constant oxygen supply while adding select foods to boost the growth of specific microorganism groups. Add carbohydrates to boost bacteria or add proteins to boost fungi (similar to what happens in our gut).

FUNGI:BACTERIA RATIOS (F:B)

Bacteria and fungi ratios are also determined by the feedstock used in the composting process. Essentially, bacteria favor the green material and the fungi the wood materials. Ideally, you should strive for a balanced fungi:bacteria ratio in your garden. Not even considering the essential role of actinomycetes, the ratio of fungi to bacteria is a window into the health of your soil and compost.

Fungi are essential to create soil structure through secretion and cross-linking nutrient cycling, and they are active carbon sequestration organisms. Bacteria are nitrogen fixers, degraders of organic matter, and form the base of the soil food web. Fungi fall into two main groups – saprophytic and mycorrhizal. Saprophytic fungi live off dead material and release nutrients held in lignin and cellulose to feed soil microbes. Mycorrhizal fungi form essential symbiotic relationships with plant roots, providing access to water and minerals otherwise unavailable to plants. The population levels of these fungi vary throughout the year. Saprophytic fungi populations go up in the fall to deal with fallen leaves. In contrast, mycorrhizal fungi populations are higher after winter – each available to meet nature's demands for growth or decomposition. Arbuscular mycorrhizal have been shown to increase a plant's immunity to viral infections.

APPLICATION OF COMPOST TEA

Use actively aerated compost tea (AACT) or non-aerated compost extract (NCE) to further extend the benefits of compost. Both are effective in adding microorganisms and essential bioavailable nutrients to your soil. It's important to note that all compost teas need to be used directly after brewing. "Bottled aerobic organisms" is a contradiction – like bottled wind.

Compost tea works exceptionally well on chemically sensitive new transplants and young seedlings, providing nutrients and active soil biota. As mentioned, compost tea effectively encourages newly planted trees and shrubs to expand their roots into the surrounding soil. Planters and vertical gardens will also benefit from compost tea.

TRENCH COMPOST

Trench compost is an anaerobic process that produces high nitrogen and phosphorous levels. Still, it's a slow process, and a lack of patience will be penalized. Planting directly on a compost trench too soon will poison your plants.

Instead, wait a year to give the ammonium a chance to dissipate or for local microorganisms to process it for you. Notwithstanding the risks, it's a brilliant way to systematically improve your soil's health profile and responsibly manage kitchen waste.

BOKASHI COMPOST

BOKASHI OVERVIEW

Bokashi is a Japanese term that implies fermented organic matter. The process is split into three phases:
- Collection process, initial fermentation, and partial dehydration
- Fermentation process using EM® effective microorganisms inoculum
- Incorporation of the fungi-rich fermented product into soil or compost to influence local biota

Bokashi composting, in my opinion, should be a universal practice in the modern home. It's a hygienic and effective way of disposing of kitchen scraps. While managing the bin requires some practice, the process should be hassle-free if you stick to the five essential rules:
- Make a healthy EM-inoculated bulking bran
- Use the inoculated bran liberally
- Keep the batch free of accumulated juices
- Increase surface area of the scraps by chopping them up and ensuring they're coated with inoculated bran after adding
- Limit air pockets – use a potato masher to press the added material down to expel water and air pockets

TRENCH COMPOSTING USING BOKASHI COMPOST

The fermented component of Bokashi significantly speeds the trench composting process up – 26 times faster. Where adding kitchen scraps untreated with EM inoculant would take 52 weeks to decompose, Bokashi fermented kitchen scraps will take only two weeks. While Bokashi is often referred to as a pickling process, pickling is essentially an acidic system. Bokashi is a fermenting process – think beer and bread.

A US gallon is about 13% of a cubic foot. You need a foot of trench for every gallon of Bokashi fermented kitchen scraps you want to bury. So, for a 5 gallon bucket of kitchen scraps, you need a 5-foot-long trench about 12 inches deep and a foot wide. Spread the content of your fermenter container across the length of your trench and cover it with soil. Suppose you're diligent in chopping your scraps up before adding them to the Bokashi bin. In that case, it will take two weeks for the microorganisms to turn your scraps into humus. If you have whole fruits in your bin, the process could take as long as five weeks. Either way, you're safe to directly plant seeds on the trench after adding the scraps. If, however, you want to transplant seedlings on the trench, wait for a minimum of two weeks for the acidity to drop before transplanting. Consider using interlocking cloche baskets to cover the new trench if you're worried about scavengers and your food scraps. Covering it with a net will help if you're using a planter.

CREATING BOKASHI COMPOST

Bokashi is a process of fermenting food scraps for composting purposes – Bokashi is not compost. To make compost from the fermented food scraps in your stabilized Bokashi bin, you need to add it to the soil. You will need:

- One part EM fermented food scraps
- Three parts of soil
- Diluted 1:10 EM inoculant
- A planter, container, or compost bag
- Half a part of aerobic compost

Mix EM Fermented Food Waste

Mix the content from the Bokashi bin with three parts of soil. Line the bottom of the planter with the half-part of compost, adding the soil and Bokashi mix on top. Cover the mix with a layer of soil before wetting the planter's content with the EM solution. Cover the top of the planter with newspaper sheets to absorb any additional moisture and then with a plastic sheet. In a month, you will have healthy soil for general purpose use.

LEAF MOLD COMPOST

Leaf mold compost, a hybrid version of leaf mold with added natural nitrogen, maximizes our harvest. Recreating that forest floor environment has many benefits for your plants. It does this in five ways:

- It improves the soil quality, so it helps against soil compaction
- It allows your plant's root system to spread out and pick up new nutrients
- It reduces plant stress as their improved root structure makes them more resilient
- It holds much more moisture in the garden, so watering is easier
- It benefits gardeners greatly because it will suppress weeds, making your life much easier

See the reference to leaf mold and under-tree composting above for more detail. Just an observation – if you're starting to switch to minimum-till practices (an essential shift), and you have plant matter on the soil surface that's not decaying, this is an indicator that your soil's microbial life (soil biota) is poor. Leaf mold compost is rich in calcium, nitrogen, potassium, phosphorus, magnesium, sulfur, and trace elements. Incorporating leaf mold into your beds increases the soil biota population diversity. It makes all those nutrients available to other microorganisms for conversion into a bioavailable format.

VERMICOMPOST

Worm castings are a slow-release, nitrogen-rich fertilizer balanced with other essential minerals – generally equivalent to 3:3:3 NPK. You can safely spread it around potted plants, vegetables, and flowing plants. If you sift it finely, adding it to your lawn would replace your usual nitrogen needs. You can also incorporate it into the soil around shrubs and trees.

It's up to you whether you want to use your compost right away or store it for the gardening season. Vermicompost can be added directly to potting soil or garden soil as a soil amendment. This makes nutrients more accessible to plants. It's possible to top dress your indoor or outdoor plants with the compost. You can also create a nutrient-loaded compost tea by straining the vermicompost in an aerated water tank for 24 hours. Don't confuse the leachate from the bottom of a poorly managed bin with composting tea. The leachate is loaded with nitrogen and should always be diluted and used with care. I advise that you test it on a single plant, review the reaction over a couple of days, and proceed if safe. Use leachate with caution, as it has the risk of poisoning your plants.

Worms are very effective at turning kitchen scraps into material high in available plant nutrients. Place it sparingly where plants can use the nutrients right away.

VERMICOMPOST IN SEED BEDS
- Sprinkle a layer along a row where the seeds are to be planted
- When planting seed trays, add vermicompost into the cell before planting
- Apply a thin layer of vermicompost on the soil of potted plants, allowing the nutrients to work down to the roots as your water. A general rule is not to apply compost against the stem or the trunk of a plant
- To create an ultra-healthy potting mix, combine one part vermicompost with one part vermiculite and two parts coconut coir. This will work well for succulents too
- Alternatively, liberally applying it to your gardening soil provides exceptional compost benefits

INOCULANTS

Inoculants can play an essential role in altering the diversity of soil biota. Introducing specifically cultivated microorganisms allows you to provide your plants with an optimized growing environment. Recent discoveries[11] of the role of mycorrhiza fungi in forests in allowing anchor trees to support weaker trees are astounding. The symphony of symbiotic organisms in EM working together for each other's benefit is another example of the magnificence of nature. While compost tea is also referred to as an inoculant, I have treated these separately as they relate more closely to the compost they're made from.

ARBUSCULAR MYCORRHIZAL
These compulsive co-workers that directly benefit plants are common in nature and have symbiotic relationships with more than 90% of plant species. AM or AMF (F for fungi) are commercially available online. They can also be introduced into your garden by growing plants that attract them, such as legumes, bahiagrass, fenugreek,

---

11   https://www.youtube.com/watch?v=iboE8UZBgkM

and lucerne. In controlled trials[12], fenugreek was most effective in colonizing AM.

EFFECTIVE MICROORGANISMS (EM®)

Using EM Consentrate

Foliage Application
Apply weekly using a clean sprayer and spray directly onto the plants, ensuring thorough wetting. This should be done in the early morning or late afternoon for best results and to prevent leaf scorch.

Soil Application
Give a good watering, ensuring the solution thoroughly wets the soil. Apply as required around mature plants or on open ground. When incorporating organic matter/ compost into the soil, apply EM dilution to the organic matter before digging in.

Compost Application
Apply to the compost heap to reduce troublesome odors and flies and to improve the compost process and quality. Preferably spray on with a hand sprayer to prevent overwetting the compost heap and apply fresh material at each addition if possible.

EM Solution

EM is a liquid concentrate, and in this form, the microorganisms are alive but dormant. It is a dark brown liquid with a pleasant vinegary, yeasty smell. The pH of this liquid is approx. 3.5. Simply dilute the concentrated solution with clean chlorine-free water to activate the EM. The EM solution produced is yellowish-brown with a pleasant smell.

Dilute EM concentrate by mixing a teaspoon of EM concentrate with a pint and a half of chlorine-free water. Apply liberally.

Adding EM To Soil
The soil biota effectiveness can be boosted by three applications of EM every fortnight after planting a crop. This will ensure a diversity in the soil biota throughout the plant's life. This will help your crop better deal with the vulnerabilities and environmental stresses like drought, heat, weeds, and pathogens.

---

12   *https://www.ijcmas.com/8-10-2019/S.B.%20Raut,%20et%20al.pdf*

Summary of Compost Use

There is growing evidence that the route taken to maximize the pedosphere's productivity was ill-informed. While modern sciences enabled us to identify the 17 nutrients required by plants, it took more than a century to unravel the complexity of biology's role in ensuring the plants had access to those nutrients. There is irrefutable proof that the use of artificial fertilizers, herbicides, and pesticides, rather than helping productivity, destroys the biological structures needed for healthy plants. This is primarily a result of our reliance on annual crops (85%) that seasonally destroyed established soil ecosystems.

That was when we were still ignorant. I am not a tree-hugging hippie (though it's probably their resilient passion that seeded some of these discoveries), but of this I am sure: if we as gardeners don't move towards mobilizing microorganisms to help us farm better, our food will increasingly have less nutrition, cost more to produce, and eventually be replaced by pills. Composting is key.

APPENDIX

GLOSSARY

Actinomycete — A group of microorganisms, intermediate between bacteria and true fungi. Generally, produce a characteristic branched mycelium, and these organisms are responsible for the earthy smell of compost (Geosmin).

Aerated static pile — Forced aeration method of composting in which a freestanding composting pile is aerated by a blower moving air through perforated pipes located beneath the pile.

Aeration — The process by which the oxygen-deficient air in compost is replaced by air from the atmosphere. Aeration can be enhanced by turning.

Aerobic — An adjective describing an organism or process that requires oxygen (for example, an aerobic organism).

Agitated-bed — An in-vessel composting method in which the material is contained in a bin or reactor and is periodically agitated by a turning machine or by augers. Some means of forced aeration is generally provided.

Ambient air temperature — The temperature of the air near the compost pile. See Composting and Soil amendment.

Ammonia (NH3) — A gaseous compound of nitrogen and hydrogen. Ammonia, which has a pungent odor, is commonly formed from organic nitrogen compounds during composting.

Ammonium (NH4 +) An ion of nitrogen and hydrogen. Ammonium is readily converted to and from ammonia depending on conditions in the compost pile.

Anaerobic An adjective describing an organism or process that does not require air or free oxygen.

Anion An atom or molecule with a negative charge (for example, nitrate, NO3).

Aspergillus fumigatus Species of a fungus with spores that cause allergic reactions in some individuals. It can also cause complications for people with existing respiratory health problems.

Archaea Microorganisms that are similar to bacteria in size and simplicity of structure but radically different in their molecular organization. They are now believed to constitute an ancient group that is intermediate between the bacteria and eukaryotes

Bacteria A group of microorganisms having single-celled or noncellular bodies. Bacteria generally appear as a spheroid, rod-like, or curved entity but occasionally appear as sheets, chains, or branched filaments.

Bedding Dry absorbent material used to provide a dry lying surface for livestock. Bedding material, such as sawdust and straw, absorb moisture from livestock waste, the soil, and the environment.

Bin composting A composting technique in which material mixtures are composted in simple structures (bins) rather than freestanding piles. Bins are considered a form of in-vessel composting, but they generally are not totally enclosed. Many composting bins include a means of forced aeration.

Biochar Charcoal that participates in biological processes and has beneficial properties for both soils and compost.

Bulk density Weight or mass per unit of volume of material made up of many individual particles. For example, the weight of a pile of wood chips divided by the volume of the pile is the bulk density. This is different from the particle density, which equals the weight of a single wood chip divided by its volume).

Bulking agent An ingredient in a mixture of composting raw material included to improve the structure and porosity of the mix. A bulking agent is generally rigid and dry and often has large particles (for example, straw). The terms bulking agent and amendment are commonly used interchangeably.

C Chemical symbol for carbon.

Carbon dioxide (CO2) An inorganic gaseous compound of carbon and oxygen. Carbon dioxide is produced by the oxidation of organic carbon compounds during composting.

Carbon-to-nitrogen ratio The ratio of the weight of organic carbon (C) to that of total nitrogen (N) in (C:N ratio) an organic material.

Cation — An atom or molecule with a positive charge (ammonium, NH4+).

Cellulose — A long chain of tightly bound sugar molecules that constitutes the chief part of the cell walls of plants.

Chemical oxygen demand (COD) — A measure of the oxygen-consuming capacity of inorganic and organic matter present in water or wastewater. It is expressed as the amount of oxygen consumed from a chemical oxidant in a specified test. It does not differentiate between stable and unstable organic matter and thus does not necessarily correlate with biochemical oxygen demand.

Compost — A group of organic residue or a mixture of organic residue and soil that has been piled, moistened, and allowed to undergo aerobic biological decomposition.

Composting — Biological degradation of organic matter under aerobic conditions to a relatively stable humus-like material called compost.

Composting amendment — An ingredient in a mixture of composting raw material included to improve the overall characteristics of the mix. Amendments often add carbon, dryness, or porosity to the mix.

Contamination — An introduction into the environment (water, air, or soil) of microorganisms, chemicals, wastes, or wastewater in a concentration that makes the environment unfit for its intended use.

Cubic yard   A unit of measure equivalent to 27 cubic feet or 22 bushels. A box that is 1 yard wide, 1 yard long, and 1 yard high and has a volume of 1 cubic yard. A cubic yard is often loosely referred to as a yard (for example, a one-yard bucket).

Curing   The final stage of composting in which stabilization of the compost continues. Still, the decomposition rate has slowed to a point where turning or forced aeration is no longer necessary. Curing generally occurs at lower mesophilic temperatures.

Damping off disease   The wilting and early death of young seedlings caused by a variety of pathogens.

Decomposers   The microorganisms and invertebrates that cause the expected degradation of natural organic materials.

Degradability   The term describes the ease and extent that a substance is decomposed by the composting process. Material that breaks down quickly and/or entirely during composting is highly degradable. Material that resists biological decomposition is considered poorly degradable or even nondegradable.

Denitrification   An anaerobic biological process that converts nitrogen compounds to nitrogen gas or nitrous oxide.

Density   The weight or mass of a substance per unit of volume.

Endotoxin   Metabolic products of gram-negative bacteria are part of the cell wall. They will remain in the bacteria after they have died.

Enzymes	Any of numerous complex proteins produced by living cells to catalyze specific biochemical reactions.
Evaporative cooling	The cooling that occurs when heat from the air or compost pile material is used to evaporate water.
Forced aeration	Can be either negatively (vacuum) or positively forced (blowers) supply of air through a composting pile.
Fungus (plural fungi)	This is a group of non-photosynthesizing plants. The nucleus of each cell is encased in a membrane. It is possible for them to form long filaments known as hyphae. Hyaline bodies can be formed by the hyphae growing together.
Gram-negative bacteria	Hans Christian Gram, a Danish physician, first developed the Gram stain procedure to distinguish pneumococci from Klebsiella pneumonia. After staining cells with crystal violet or gentian violet, a solution of iodine is applied. The cytoplasm of bacteria is stained purple by this method. A decolorizing agent is then applied to the cells that had been stained with crystal violet and iodine. The permeability of Gram-positive and Gram-negative bacteria to these purple iodine-dye complexes when they are treated with the decolorizing solvent is the main difference between the two. After treatment with the decolorizing agent, Gram-positive bacteria retain purple iodine-dye complexes, whereas Gram-negative bacteria do not.
Grinding	Operation that reduces the particle size of material. Grinding implies that particles are broken apart primarily by smashing and crushing rather than tearing or slicing.

Humus   The dark or black carbon-rich, relatively stable residue resulting from the decomposition of organic matter.

HAPs   Hazardous Air Pollutants. There are 188 HAPs on the EPA's list, including at least 29 HAPs that have been quantified in composting air emissions. The kinds and quantities of HAPs tend to be a function of feedstocks, with biosolids composting having the most carefully and thoroughly studied air emission profiles.

Hydrogen sulfide (H2S)   A gas with the characteristic odor of rotten eggs produced by anaerobic decomposition.

Hydrolysis   The word literally means *unbinding by water*. It is when water is involved in breaking chemical bonds. In plant biology the process results in complex compounds reduced to monomers.

Immobilization, nitrogen   Conversion of nutrient compounds from an inorganic form, available to plants, into the organic tissue of microorganisms (or other plants). The nutrients are unavailable until the microorganisms die and the nutrients' microbial tissues decompose. Nitrogen immobilization occurs when a material with a high C:N ratio is land applied. The microorganisms that use the carbon also assimilate the available nitrogen, rendering it unavailable to plants.

Inoculum (plural inocula)   Living organisms or material containing living organisms (bacteria or other microorganisms) that are added to initiate or accelerate a biological process (for example, biological seeding).

In-vessel composting A diverse group of composting methods uses various vessels to compost materials in a containerized environment. These include reactors for biofuels.

Ion An electrically charged atom or molecule. Ions may be positively charged (cation) or negatively charged (anion).

K Chemical symbol for potassium.

Land application Application of manure, sewage sludge, municipal wastewater, and industrial waste to land either for ultimate disposal or for reuse of the nutrients and organic matter for their fertilizer value.

Leachate The liquid that results when water comes in contact with a solid extracts material, either dissolved or suspended, from the solid.

Lignin A substance that forms the woody cell walls of plants and the cementing material between them. Lignin is resistant to decomposition.

Litter, poultry Dry absorbent bedding material, such as straw, sawdust, and wood shavings, spread on poultry barn floors to absorb waste. The manure-bedding combination from the barn is referred to as litter.

Manure The fecal and urinary excretion of livestock and poultry. Sometimes referred to as livestock waste. This material may also contain bedding, spilled feed, water, or soil. It may also include waste not associated with livestock excrete, such as milking center wastewater, contaminated milk, hair, feathers, or other debris.

Microorganism An organism requiring magnification to be seen.

Moisture content   The fraction or percentage of a substance made up of water. Moisture content equals the weight of the water part divided by the total weight (water plus dry matter part). Moisture content is sometimes reported on a dry basis. Dry-basis moisture content equals the weight of the water divided by the weight of the dry matter.

Monomers   Natural monomers are amino acids from proteins and monosaccharides from carbohydrates, amongst others.

Mulch   A material spread over the soil surface to conserve moisture and porosity in the soil underneath and to suppress weed growth. Grass clippings, compost, wood chips, bark, sawdust, and straw are common mulch material.

N   Chemical symbol for nitrogen.

Nitrate-nitrogen   A negatively charged ion made up of nitrogen and oxygen (NO_3-). Nitrate is a water-soluble and mobile form of nitrogen. Because of its negative charge, soil particles are not firmly held and leached away.

Nitrification   The biochemical oxidation of ammonia nitrogen to nitrate.

Nutrient-holding capacity   The ability to absorb and retain nutrients is available to the roots of plants.

Organic matter   Chemical substances of animal or vegetable origin contain hydrocarbons and their derivatives.

P   Chemical symbol for phosphorus.

Passive aeration	Air movement through composting windrows and piles occurs by natural forces, including convection, diffusion, wind, and the tendency of warm air to rise (thermal buoyancy).
Passive composting	Method of composting: There is little management and manipulation of the materials after they are mixed and piled. Turning infrequently occurs (for example, monthly). Forced aeration is not provided.
Passively aerated windrow	A composting method in which windrows are constructed over a series of composting perforated plastic pipes that serve as air ducts for passive aeration. Windrows are not turned.
Pathogen	Any organism capable of producing disease or infection. Often found in waste material, most pathogens are killed by the high temperatures of the composting process.
Peat	Unconsolidated soil material consisting mainly of organic matter accumulated under excessive moisture conditions. The organic matter is not decomposed or is only slightly decomposed.
pH	A measure of hydrogen ions' concentration in a solution, expressed as a number between 0 and 14. A number below 7 indicates acidity, and above 7 indicates basicity (alkalinity). A pH of 7 is considered neutral.
Phytotoxic	An adjective describing a substance that has a toxic effect on plants. Immature or anaerobic compost may contain phytotoxins (acids or alcohols) harmful to seedlings or sensitive plants.

Pollution | The presence in a body of water (or soil or air) of a substance (pollutant) in such quantities that it impairs the body's usefulness or renders it offensive to the senses of sight, taste, or smell. In general, a public-health hazard may be created. Still, only economic or aesthetics are involved in some instances, as when foul odors pollute the air.

Porosity | A measure of the pore space of a material or pile of materials. Porosity is equal to the volume of the pores divided by the total volume. In composting, the term porosity is sometimes used loosely, referring to the volume of the pores occupied by air only (without including the pore space occupied by water).

Primary substrate | The main waste material that requires treatment. Also called primary raw material.

Primary Pythium | A fungal plant pathogen that causes seed, seedling, and root rots on many plants. These fungi are most active under conditions of high moisture.

Recipe | The ingredients and proportions used in blending together several raw materials for composting.

Root rot | A disease of plants characterized by discoloration and decay of the roots.

Saprophytes | Live on dead or dying organic matter and obtain their energy by breaking plant and animal material down.

Saturated paste   A laboratory technique in which solid particles are rendered into a paste so that characteristics, such as pH and soluble salt concentration, can be measured.

Semi-solid manure   Manure that has had some bedding added or has received sufficient air drying to raise the solids content, enabling it to be stacked.

Shredding   An operation that reduces the particle size of material and increases the surface area.

Soil conditioner   A soil additive that improves the soil's resistance to erosion, increases its permeability to air and water, improves its texture, its resistance to surface compaction, and improves tilth.

Soil structure   The combination or arrangement of primary soil particles into secondary particles, units, or peas. Compost helps bind primary soil particles to improve the structure of the soil.

Stability of compost   The rate of change or decomposition of compost. Generally, stability refers to the lack of change or resistance to change. A stable compost continues to decompose slowly and has a low oxygen demand.

Structure of composting mix   The ability to resist settling and compaction. Structure is improved by adding raw material or large particles.

Texture of composting mix   Characteristic that describes the available surface area of particles. A fine or raw material texture implies many small particles with a large combined surface area. A course texture implies large particles with less overall surface area.

Thermophilic   Heat-loving microorganisms that thrive in and generate temperatures above 105 degrees Fahrenheit (40 °C).

Trench composting   Incorporation of non-fatty food waste into soil for anaerobic digestion. Also known as soil incorporation composting.

Turning   A composting operation that mixes and agitates material in a windrow pile or vessel. Its main aeration effect is to increase the porosity of the windrow to enhance passive aeration. It can be accomplished with bucket loaders or specially designed turning machines.

Vermin   Noxious or objectionable animals, insects, or other pests, especially small ones such as rats, mice, and flies.

VOCs   Volatile Organic Compounds. Organic compounds or substances vaporize at relatively low temperatures, including alcohol, methane, and ammonia. Volatile compounds are rapidly lost from the composting pile environment.

Windrow   A long, relatively narrow, and low pile. Windrows have a large, exposed surface area that encourages passive aeration and drying.

Yard waste   Leaves, grass clippings, yard trimmings, and other organic garden debris.

CONVERSION TABLES

LINEAR MEASUREMENT (LENGTH & DISTANCE)

IMPERIAL	METRIC	METRIC	IMPERIAL
1 inch	25.4 millimeters (mm)	1 millimeter (mm)	0.0384 inch
1 foot (1 foot = 12 inches)	0.3048 meter (m)	1 centimeter (1cm = 10mm)	0.3837 incch
1 yard (3 feet)	0.9144 meter (m)	1 meter (1m = 100cm)	1.0936 yards
1 mile (1760 yards)	1.6093 kilometer (km)	1 kilometer (1km = 1000m)	0.6214 miles

AREA MEASUREMENT

IMPERIAL	METRIC	METRIC	IMPERIAL
1 square inch	6.4516 cm^2	1 square centimeter (cm^2)	0.155 square inches
1 square foot (144 square inches)	92.9 cm^2	1 square meter (1m2 = 10,000cm^2)	1.196 square yards
1 square yard (9 square feet)	0.8361 m^2	1 hectare (1ha = 10,000m^2)	2.47 acres
1 acre (4840 square yards)	0.040469 hectare	1 square kilometer (1km2 = 100ha)	247.105 acres
1 square mile (640 acres)	259 hectares		

CUBIC MEASUREMENT (VOLUME)

IMPERIAL	METRIC	METRIC	IMPERIAL
1 cubic inch	16.4 cc or cm^3	1 cubic centimeter (cc or cm^3)	0.0610 cubic inches
1 cubic foot (1728 in.^{3})	0.0283 m^3	1 cubic meter (1 million cm^3)	1.308 cubic yards
1 cubic yard (27 ft.^{3})	0.765 m^3		

CAPACITY MEASURE (VOLUME)

IMPERIAL	METRIC	METRIC	IMPERIAL
1 (imperial) fl. oz. (1/20 imperial pint)	28.41ml	0.5 litre (5cm^3)	1.056 US pint
1 (US liquid) fl. oz. (1/16 US pint)	29.57ml	1 litre (10cm^3)	2.11 US pints
1 (imperial) pint (20 fl. oz.)	568.26ml		
1 (US liquid) pint (16 fl. oz.)	473.18ml		
1 (imperial) gallon (4 quarts)	4.546 litre		
1 (US liquid) gallon (4 quarts)	3.785 litre		

MASS (WEIGHT)

IMPERIAL	METRIC	METRIC	IMPERIAL
1 ounce	28.35 gram	1 gram (1,000mg)	15.43 grain
1 pound (10 ounces)	0.3545 kilogram	1 kilogram (1,000g)	2.205 pounds
1 ton (2240 lbs)	1.016 tonnes	1 tonne (1,000kg)	0.984 ton

TEMPERATURE

FAHRENHEIT	CELCIUS	CELCIUS	FAHRENHEIT
32^0F	0.0^0C	-20^0C	-4^0F
40^0F	4.4^0C	-10^0C	14^0F
50^0F	10.0^0C	0^0C	32^0F
55^0F	12.8^0C	10^0C	50^0F
60^0F	15.6^0C	20^0C	68^0F
70^0F	21.1^0C	30^0C	86^0F
77^0F	25.0^0C	40^0C	104^0F
90^0F	32.2^0C	50^0C	122^0F
105^0F	40.6^0C	60^0C	140^0F
120^0F	48.9^0C	70^0C	158^0F
140^0F	60.0^0C	80^0C	176^0F
145^0F	62.8^0C	90^0C	194^0F
150^0F	65.6^0C	100^0C	212^0F
160^0F	71.1^0C	110^0C	230^0F

METRIC TO IMPERIAL CONVERSION

Convert	To	Multiply by
Kilometers	Miles	0.62
Kilometers	Feet	3280.8
Meters	Feet	3.28
Centimeters	Inches	0.39
Millimeters	Inches	0.039
Liters	Quarts	1.057
Liters	Gallons	0.264
Milliliters	Cups	0.0042
Milliliters	Ounces	0.0338
Celsius	Fahrenheit	°C x 9/5 + 32 = °F
Kilogram	Tons	0.0011
Kilogram	Pounds	2.2046
Grams	Ounces	0.035
Grams	Pounds	0.002205
Milligrams	Ounces	0.000035

IMPERIAL TO METRIC CONVERSION

Convert	To	Multiply by
Fahrenheit	Celsius	$(°F - 32) \times 5/9 = °C$
Inches	Meters	0.0254
Inches	Centimeters	2.54
Inches	Millimeters	25.4
Feet	Meters	0.3
Yards	Meters	0.91
Yards	Kilometers	0.00091
Miles	Kilometers	1.61
Ounces	Milliliters	29.57
Cups	Milliliters	236.6
Quarts	Liters	0.95
Gallons	Liters	3.785
Ounces	Milligrams	28350
Ounces	Grams	28.35
Pounds	Kilograms	0.454
Tons	Kilograms	907.18

HELPFUL WEIGHTS

I advise that you keep your compost at 50% moisture throughout until used (within six months of making it).

A full cubic-yard-sized bin (the size of a standard composting bin) will produce just over 12 cubic feet of compost weighing about 150 pounds – enough to cover 150 square feet of soil an inch deep.

Compost weighs approximately 12.5 pounds per cubic foot (specific gravity 0.2).

A spread of 0.5 inches thick will cover 300 sq. ft. from a single composted pile of three cubic foot (1 cubic yard).

An application of 0.5 inches is adequate for annual bed maintenance.

EPILOGUE

I sincerely hope that this book becomes a tool that aids gardeners in appreciating the infinite wisdom of mother nature in providing the world with microorganisms. Ideally, I hope that your skills at proliferating these organisms have improved to produce healthy soil for healthy gardens to provide healthy food.

It's impossible to overemphasize the importance of composting, both for your garden and the general environment. As such, your skill at creating good compost, using various methods, materials, and microorganisms, is inextricably linked to becoming a master gardener. Together we have explored all the domains of this vast topic in some detail.

I have made every effort to ensure both novice and experienced gardeners will benefit from this book. I have tried to tier practical learning and theoretical information progressively throughout. The perfection of your skills is a matter of practice.

While this book is sufficiently comprehensive to be used as a single source of learning, I hope to take your learning further with my Composting Masterclass Course. You can find out more about the Composting Masterclass Course at : simplifygardening.com/compostingmasterclass

Printed in Great Britain
by Amazon

18132247R00154